WOMEN

This book will give you all the important things you need to know about female orgasm. What is the difference between clitoral and vaginal orgasm? Where orgasm happens and how. What muscles are involved and how to strengthen them and control them. How to adapt lovemaking techniques for a more orgasmic climate. How to change the language of lovemaking from sexual, which involves genitals, to sensual—which involves people. How to deal with problems like lubrication, menstruation, or menopause. How to avoid performance anxiety. And much more.

MEN

If loving a woman is important to you, this is a book you must read, too. It is the other half of your love story . . .

Other Delilah Books

OLDER WOMAN/YOUNGER MAN
ORGASM

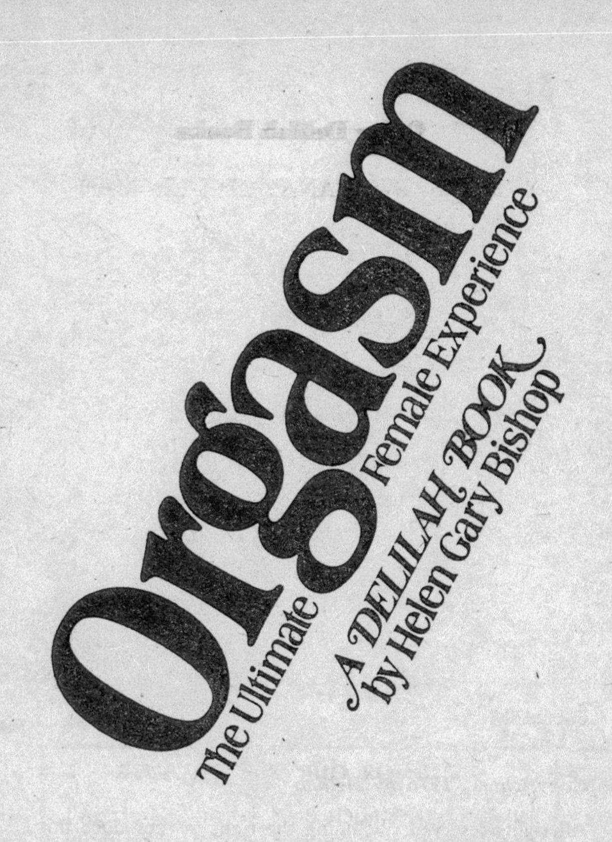

PINNACLE BOOKS • NEW YORK CITY

ORGASM

An original Pinnacle Books edition, published for the first time anywhere.

ISBN: 0-523-00837-6

First printing, April 1976

Printed in the United States of America

PINNACLE BOOKS, INC.
275 Madison Avenue
New York, N. Y. 10016

CONTENTS

Introduction
A Typical Girlhood 1
Love American Style 9
Freud's Heavy Hand 13
Movies Take Over 18
Sexual Revolution 23
The Big Lie 28
One. Anatomy of the Female Orgasm 33
Two. The Vaginal Versus Clitoral Conflict 44
Three. The PC Factor 54
Four. The Sex Flex 64
Sex Flex Exercises 68
Five. Slow & Easy: The Cure for Rabbit Fever 71
Six. Any Woman Can—But Not With Dr. Reuben 85
Seven. The Juicy Blues 104
Eight. Masturbation: End Your Fear of Flying Solo 112
Nine. Journey to the Pleasure Zones 121
Ten. Extra-Sexory Perception 127
Eleven. Kicks & Kinks 134
Twelve. Sex Without Orgasm???? 140
Epilogue
Still a Long Way to Go 148

ORGASM

INTRODUCTION

A TYPICAL GIRLHOOD

The first time I had an orgasm I was twenty-four years old. Up until then I couldn't understand what all the fuss was about. I was confused by all I had heard and read about women leaving home, husband, and children to follow a good-for-nothing who could "make them come." I remember the gossips in my home town pointing to a society girl who had fallen from grace by marrying a hairdresser instead of her fiancé, the banker's son. "That's what happens to a girl who gets carried away with *physical* love," they said. To my young ears it made physical love sound very dangerous for women and I must have made an unconscious decision to try and avoid it at all costs. This may have been a factor which kept me from having an orgasm until well into my sexual life.

Physical love as opposed to what? Emotional, spiritual, intellectual love, weren't they all the same thing? How could an overwhelming physical experience wipe out all will and reason? I couldn't understand anything except that of all the obstacles to the development of a woman's independence and spirit, including pregnancy, *being carried away by physical love* seemed the most dangerous!

The danger just made the "forbidden fruit" that much more exciting, of course, and I remember how my teen-aged heart pounded when the inevitable happened and I found myself alone for the first time with a young boy who was caressing me. I kept saying to myself "Don't let this get out of hand. Don't allow him to go too far. Don't lose control." Naturally I forgot all the "don'ts" and started kissing and caressing him right back, my hands groping his body just as furiously as his were mine. There I was, doing what everyone said was sure to get a girl into trouble—petting. I loved it.

Afterward, however, I had very mixed feelings. "I'm a pushover," I thought. I hadn't put up any kind of real resistance at all. I had let him get away with murder, and what was worse, I had encouraged him! He would lose his respect for me, tell all his pals that I'm easy. I was convinced I was a thoroughly "bad girl" who'd end up badly, never catch a "decent" boy, and certainly never get married.

My friend Jimmy didn't lose his respect for me, however. He was more solicitous than ever and we had a wild crush on each other. I was all of fifteen and for a full two weeks my days began and ended with thoughts of Jimmy, and marriage and forever after. I was convinced that the magic of Jimmy's unique personality was responsible for my having forgotten and forsaken years of teachings and warnings about what not to do with boys. But then Jimmy got the measles and I went to a football game where I met—Johnny.

Johnny was different from Jimmy in every possible way. He was tall and athletic; Jimmy was sort of skinny and bookish. Johnny loved jazz and Jimmy listened to classical only. So there I was after having sworn myself to Jimmy and Brahms I was swinging with Johnny and Brubeck. Petting with Johnny was *much more* exciting than with Jimmy and I was grateful to the powers that be for having arranged this happy accident which lead me to my chance meeting with the *true* love of my life. I would have gone and "given myself" to Jimmy, married him and everything without ever having known *real* passion. Then Johnny broke his leg and I met—I can't quite remember his name but he was wonderful.

After a while part of the truth began to sink in—perhaps I should restate that—part of the lies I had been told about how women feel about sex was becoming visible to me. I began to realize that I had a sex drive all my own and that being in the presence of an attractive boy turned it on. Because of the speed at which my passions came and went, I also began to realize that there must be a difference between "being in love" and experiencing an overwhelming physical desire. Although I didn't understand it at the time I was starting to sense the difference between passion and love. So an underlying anxiety still remained that the day LOVE would happen to me I would be carried away, lose all control, be a toy in the hands of the master of my body and soul. Sexually I was saving myself for "true love." I necked and petted wildly as did all my friends, but I carefully kept from "going all the way" until the really real thing came along. His name was Henry. It happened in our last year of high school. We were both seventeen.

By the age of seventeen I had a good idea of what my interests were and what kind of movies and books I liked and what I wanted to study in college. My own personality was taking shape, in other words. So when I met Henry and discovered we shared many of the same interests, I wasn't just going along for the ride—we actually did have a lot in common. We met in December and became lovers in the spring. We packed a picnic and Henry brought a blanket and out to the country we went in Henry's father's car. Somehow neither of us was very hungry and as we started to caress each other, a strangeness set in that made everything seem less natural. I had my eyes tightly shut as Henry lay down beside me. "Please be careful. Don't come inside me. Don't hurt me. Stop if I ask you to, please." Poor Henry. It's a wonder he was able to do anything at all. All of a sudden our fears had taken over our passion. When Henry finally penetrated, it was painful for both of us. "I'm sorry I came so quickly," he said, having read somewhere that that was a cardinal sin in men. I was grateful he had. Relieved to have gotten that out of the way, we ate up our picnic.

Despite the disappointing beginnings we kept at it and got a lot better. After a month or so I stopped hurting and started experiencing a lot of pleasure during lovemaking. For Henry it was much better than for me because he always had an orgasm and try as we might, it kept on eluding me. But I was in love and although the satisfaction of total release escaped me, the excitement of sexual discovery made up for it. I was at least certain that sex was something I enjoyed, and would some day enjoy to complete satisfaction. My idyllic first love affair lasted over a year, into our first year of college. Then we both began to find out that there was a whole world of interesting people around us. Exclusive togetherness was keeping us from discovering both the world and ourselves. We decided to date other people "just for curiosity" and eventually with a little bit of torment and tears, we went our separate ways. We have remained friends to this day.

The fear of losing control to blind love lingered on. Although this had not happened to me with Henry, I attributed it to his having been as inexperienced as I. I was his first lover also. I worried about meeting an older, experienced man who would know all the tricks needed to manipulate me. By this time I knew I was made for a life of travel, adventure, and career and I didn't want "settling down" to interfere.

Until the fateful day in my twenty-fourth year I had been so successful in keeping control of my feelings that nothing extraordinary happened, not emotionally and I'm afraid, not sexually. My experiences had been varied, rewarding, amusing, educational, exciting—but no orgasms. I certainly did enjoy sex; the warmth, intimacy, and lovingness of it made it a very important part of my life. However the excitement and the hope for an unexpected something remained unfulfilled. I was active and consequently distracted enough not to be physically unhappy about it. Also I was beginning to think that maybe everybody was exaggerating and that the reality of sexual satisfaction was, as in other things, a peg or two lower than fantasy. I decided I wasn't going to worry about it.

I had thought a lot about why I had not had orgasms as I settled for unclimactic sex as something pleasurable if not totally satisfying. I suspected as I'm sure a lot of women have that there was something wrong with me. I mean that I wasn't quite screwed together right, as it were. I wasn't above thinking it may have been my partner's fault but with my lover at that time, I had to discount that. Lew was a real ace, a perfect combination of tense and tender, and built exactly to my specifications. Furthermore we loved each other, which made things even more delightful. I was an aspiring young actress and he a director. We shared a passion for the theater which drew us even closer together. I had my own studio apartment and his loft was just a short ten-minute walk away. It was *La Bohème*, I was Mimi and he was Rudolphe and life was a lark. But there I was; over a year of practically living together and those bells kept on not ringing. And then . . .

Lew had just made me some espresso coffee and we were listening to the coolest jazz while a quiet rainfall clouded his skylight. We had spent a lovely day walking on a sunny beach and jumping in for a swim the second we felt like it. It had been one of those perfect weekends you wish could go on for another week. We were alone together, the lights dim, the music soft. The morning was very far away. We started making love with the natural ease of two people who know each other very well. My skin was still warm from the sun and the cool sheets felt delicious as we rocked on them, wrapped around each other. Then something different started to happen to me.

A tingling sensation in the toes quickly overtook the rest of me with the power of an avalanche. Lew realized something was different and started whispering words of encouragement. "That's right, babe, let yourself go . . . easy does it, don't rush." The tingling finally settled into tension in that area I had previously thought of as a mere launching pad. "My pussy's on fire," I heard myself saying.

I couldn't believe the language I had just used. That word was so "bad" when I was a child. It felt so good to use it, such a release. I got bolder but I could barely breathe, let alone talk. "My cunt's gone crazy." I must have gone on babbling as the tension grew to near pain. A flash went through my head—"This may be it! This may be IT!"—and for a fleeting moment I was afraid that thinking about it would make it go away.

Lew grabbed my hips as he moved inside me more insistently. Each movement of his steady thrusting became more distinct. His cock seemed to become hotter, thicker as it pushed in, filling me fuller, then moved out, pulling me out of myself. Then spasms of pleasure ran through my whole body, up through my abdomen and chest and shoulders and down through my thighs and legs. "I think I'm coming," I managed to gasp. He smiled at me and my screams of pleasure so surprised him that he started to laugh. And then I laughed too, even as the tears rolled down my cheeks.

I was amazed to discover how devastating orgasms could be. It suddenly gave a new meaning, new importance to lovemaking. For a full week I thought of virtually nothing else. The feelings of relief I felt were also a surprise to me. I guess I was more worried about not having orgasms than I thought I was. I did have a moment of resentment at all the lost time when I could have been experiencing divine orgasms, but that didn't last long. After all, it wasn't as if I hadn't been enjoying sex.

I remember the time, long before orgasm, when I began to really enjoy sex. Although I indulged in the great American pastime, petting, it wasn't until I was well out of the familial foyer that I felt free enough of both guilt and surveillance to venture forth toward my true sexual identity. But feelings of somehow being a "bad girl," dirty, brazen, and embarrassed about making love lingered on. The image of the "bad girl" as opposed to the "good" was something that my friends and I were carefully lectured on as early as grade school. In high school, we all knew there were girls who "did" and the rest who "didn't." Most of us who "didn't" felt very smug with just a tinge of jealousy.

A girl named Sally was well-known for being fast. She was proud of "putting out" and bragged once in the locker room that her boyfriend Chris "could see where the sun doesn't shine" any time he wanted to. At the time, I was speechless with shock. How could she do it and then brag about it? Why wasn't she ashamed or afraid of getting caught? How come she talked as though she actually enjoyed it? I longed to ask her questions. She knew so many things I didn't know. Sally did get "caught" by pregnancy and became the talk of the school. But a year after graduation she got married in a big church ceremony, dressed in a long white gown. Sally knew a lot more than I ever imagined.

Getting away to college and free-swinging dormitory life helped to clear the way for a less furtive, less guilt-ridden sex life. The freedom from guilt paved the way for pleasure naturally. But still the right to pleasure seemed to belong more to men than to girls. One night I was with Bob who was a graduate assistant (I was into older men!) and after lovemaking he said, "Boy, you really dig it, don't you? I can't tell you how great it is to be with a girl who can let go and enjoy herself." At first I was flattered at such a compliment from a sophisticated older person who was practically a part of the administration. Later I started thinking however and as I did, I got very mad. Why should I consider a remark like that such a compliment? Why didn't I feel right from the beginning that enjoying sex was my absolute right? Who or what made me feel I was doing something wrong and was not behaving like a good girl should behave? That bit of introspection set the stage for a long head trip on the subject of female pleasure and orgasm and why its appearance, acceptance, and appreciation is such a recent event.

LOVE AMERICAN STYLE

Growing up in America has entitled us to a heavy inheritance of rigid sexual Do's and Don'ts from our British ancestors. George Bernard Shaw gave it the blanket name of middle-class morality. Whatever you call it, it's a bad piece of baggage. But our British underpinnings can't be blamed forever. We have to start taking some of the responsibility, and more important, start making changes. While men in American society have not been under the same pressures as women to keep virginal until marriage and absolutely faithful afterward, they have reacted to the "sex is dirty" conditioning with their own hang-ups. It's time to call a spade a spade. And when we run into male hang-ups, that's exactly what we should do. An experience I had is a perfect example.

I had just returned to New York after a number of years' residence in France. Some friends introduced me to a dashing international lawyer, thinking we'd have lots in common. We did, and we soon became lovers but in a rather fleeting way since he shared an apartment with a roommate and was nervous about making noises "too revealing." One night, on our third or fourth date, the roommate was away and I thought "At last, we're alone!" To my surprise out went the light and up went the hi-fi as usual. I switched a night light on just as my lover was removing his pants. He glared at me. "What on earth are you doing?"

"I just wanted to watch you undress." His mouth fell open in utter disbelief and he said, "For God's sake, don't be tacky." That was the first time I had felt kind of dirty in almost ten years. As I dressed and got ready to leave, he tried to reason with me, explaining that all he wanted to do was make love, not exhibitionism. I replied, "The sight of the naked body is part of lovemaking for me, and I resent being called tacky because of it." He told me that no woman had ever said that to him before and he'd never "had any complaints." I told him to put my name at the top of the list, and left.

Once my rage subsided, I began to ask myself why I let a sexual retard like my lawyer friend make me feel dirty. He obviously had a guilt trip about sex. That's why he had to "do it" in the dark, with music drowning out the noises. I felt justified in calling him down for it. But why should his uptight behavior affect me? I think the answer was a certain amount of conditioning that surfaced suddenly with this humiliating experience. The point I'm making is that even though consciously I knew I was acting naturally, normally, the layers of guilt about sex go so deep that a man pointing a finger, even a man obviously screwed up on the subject, could stir up doubts.

When and why did the double standard come into existence? Why would men deliberately suppress the natural instincts of woman, thus depriving themselves of eager, accessible partners? It probably began when men discovered that there was a connection between sexual intercourse and babies. Before then it was thought that women became pregnant when they matured and came into season, somewhat like fruit trees. The ability to impregnate meant the ability to produce another pair of working hands for the fields. A larger family meant more power for the man who was at the head of it. When private property came into being, it was important to have heirs to pass it along to. Men automatically commandeered the family unit because the women were kept busy breeding. Since the male heirs would inherit land and property it was essential that their paternity be authentic. Thus the absolute fidelity of the wife was something that had to be assured at all costs. The circle was complete.

Laws came into being to punish adulterous women. Unwritten laws known as traditions and mores followed, all shaping the woman's role into that of an obedient, virtuous, chaste creature. This kind of woman became the "right" kind of candidate for a wife. With her the continuance of a pure strain and male authority was not put into question. She was a "safe" kind of woman. The other kind, the wilful, independent woman who expressed her mind and her senses freely, mindless of society's rules, was the "wrong" kind of woman. Ironically the rarer she became, the more desirable she was. Men set about getting "good" women to the altar and "bad" women to bed. The stereotypes of the vamp and the virgin acquired the images of popular culture in Western civilization.

Since marriage became the most available and most desirable job opportunity for women, girl children were taught directly and indirectly to desire marriage. They were carefully advised on the differences between good and bad girls with heavy emphasis on the sexual aspects of these. Feminine wiles became part of the weaker sex's charm and were put copiously to use in attracting the necessary husband. The smart young lady teased her way into her young man's sexual fantasies, but if he wanted "the real thing" he had to marry her to get it. This sexual trading off, while it assured the continuation of the institution of marriage and private property, seriously set back our society's sexual development, especially that of women.

What opportunities did young people have to experiment and thereby discover their sexual identities? A young girl, rigidly channeled into marriage and monogamy, was expected to find sexual satisfaction in her husband's bed. The young men themselves had access to limited and usually poor training ground, either the local loose girl or cat house. Venereal disease was a big deterrent for both the men and married women tempted to experiment outside of marriage. And women had an added deterrent—fear of pregnancy. In order to keep them on the straight and narrow path, girls were made to feel that for women sex was a duty, something to be put up with, something distasteful, humiliating, culminating in childbirth which could be painful if not downright fatal. This did not make for a very erotic climate in young America. While the men were free to "play around," sowing their wild oats before marriage and paying for the favors of fancy women afterward, their wives had to do with what they had at home, good, bad, or indifferent.

FREUD'S HEAVY HAND

The obvious result of this situation was tremendous sexual frustration for women. How did they react? The names for their psychosomatic illnesses are many and colorful. "Miseries" and "vapours" were afflictions of both our Southern belles and Victorian ladies. By any other name, the combination of feelings of shame, frustration, and rage set the stage for much real mental and physical unbalance. In Europe where psychological and psychosomatic disorders had not yet gotten the name of neurosis, the label "hysteria" was affixed to the manifestations of women's dissatisfactions.

The word comes from the Greek *hysterikos*, meaning uterus. The theory was that erratic, uncontrolled behavior in women was a direct result of the functioning of their childbearing organ. This was a neat way of categorizing females as irresponsible biologically and limiting their role in society to that of wife/mother/lover. Then Freud came along and gave his stamp of approval to traditional roles in the official language of science with his "biology is destiny" theory.

> **Nature has determined woman's destiny through beauty, charm, and sweetness.***

Freud did not see clearly into women's sexuality nor their desires for equality as he admitted to Marie Bonaparte (after having spent thirty years developing theories on the subject). He recognized sexuality starting with infancy, and he occasionally catalogued the ill effects of official morality. But he never seriously questioned the basis of patriarchal family life nor the (sometimes unfortunate but always desirable) *necessity to preserve a chaste and sexually inactive young womanhood.*

He was, in America especially, the rationalizer of the invidious relationship between the sexes, the ratifier of traditional roles. His theory of "penis envy" alone set women back for generations. Freud believed he had found the key to feminine experience—in that moment when girls discover they are "castrated"—a "momentous discovery which little girls are destined to make":

> **They notice the penis of a brother or playmate strikingly visible and of large proportions, at once recognize it as the superior counterpart of their own small and inconspicuous organ, and from that time forward fall a victim to envy for the penis.†**

From this theory, he concluded:

> **Women regard themselves as wronged from infancy, as undeservedly cut short and set back; and the em-**

---

*Letters of Sigmund Freud.

†Freud, "Some Psychological Consequences of the Anatomical Distinctions between the Sexes."

bitterment of so many daughters against their mothers derives, in the last analysis, from the reproach against her of having brought them into the world as women instead of as men.‡

This theory is absurd today, but its effect on psychoanalytical development and practice and, in turn, its influence and translation into common thought and action is incalculable. Freud was very much a product of the male-oriented, upper-class society of his time. He attributed to women the traditional submissive role and those who rebelled against it were considered maladjusted or downright neurotic. Speaking privately, in a letter to Marie Bonaparte, Freud admitted:

. . . the great question that has never been answered and which I have not been able to answer despite my thirty years of research into the feminine soul, is "What does a woman want?"*

In view of such basic uncertainty it was very unfortunate indeed that Freud went as far as he did in formulating a concept of female psychology. As of that time, the medical and psychiatric profession formed a kind of cabal to keep women in their place and society's structure intact.

Even as women were encouraged, even pressured to take pride in childbearing and motherhood, the organ of this function became a cross to bear. Pregnancy, birth, and the menstrual period were considered female afflictions, and pointed at as proof of female inferiority. Women were made to feel ashamed of their menstrual flow and girls were ostracized and treated "differently" when they "became women." The menstrual blood was thought to be "bad" blood and was referred to as women's *curse*, a word still used today. Some other

---

‡Collected papers of Sigmund Freud.

**The Life and Work of Sigmund Freud*, quote from a letter.

choice expressions coming down to us through the ages to remind us of our inferiority are: "unclean," "the red devil," "falling off the roof," and "unwell" just to name a few. They all have the idea of dirty, painful, or bad news in common and are certainly not calculated to help little girls take pride and expect pleasure from their sexual organs.

This association with dirty or unmentionable explains women's traditional reluctance to talk about or look at their genitals. Little boys are always showing off their penises for each other. Their parents make light of a "boys will be boys" pastime. But should they find out that their daughter is comparing pussies with her girlfriends, she would be made to understand that it isn't done, it's a dirty thing to do. So women grow up not wanting to touch their private parts except for practical, hygienic purposes. Recently a painter friend of mine, who is happily married to a painter also and has two grown children, said to me: "You know, a gynecologist just made me look at myself down there. I never realized how beautiful it was."

My own awareness of my genital beauty came at the age of twenty-five. I went to bed with a somewhat older, sophisticated art dealer. When he had barely just seen me naked, he immediately turned his attentions southward. "Oh, I knew you would look like this," he said, peering into what I thought of as merely my bush. I was reluctant, embarrassed, at first.

He explained, "A woman's sex is not just a hole. It is color, texture, form, taste, smell, and all the while it responds, reacts, comments. It is as revealing of her personality as the way she walks, uses her face. Yours is beautiful." Then he proceeded to show me his collection of cunt pictures and paintings. I was thrilled to be compared with these works of art. There was no doubt about it, he was a connoisseur. If you have any doubt about how interesting your "other lips" are, get a friend to take a Polaroid picture of you there, before and after sex, and check the fascinating, beautiful differences for yourself.

Just as women sought to hide or down-play their genitals, they attempted to compensate by showing off the more acceptable female physical attributes. The amount of brainwashing we have been subjected to concerning our contours defies imagination. A quick scan of any book illustrating the costumes of women through the ages will show the changes shapes underwent in order to stay in fashion (which is another way of saying to stay desirable to men).

MOVIES TAKE OVER

One of the most dramatic areas is the bustline to designers and the breasts to you and me. Full, aggressive breasts were the hallmark of the pin-up so popular with the boys overseas during the Second World War. The lonely, sex-starved G.I. longing for an idealized, exaggerated feminine creature turned the pin-up into the sex-object body admired through the fifties (Betty Grable, Rita Hayworth) right into the sixties (Brigitte Bardot, Sophia Loren). Women were constantly comparing their figures, especially their bustlines, to these epitomes of feminine beauty. Psychologists were saying that the emphasis on mammaries was a sign of insecurity and search for the protective mother's breast. One writer gave it a name: Breast Quest. Women fell right in with the big-boob fever and the padded bra industry made a fortune.

The movie stars and industry did more than just dictate the kind of figures and faces we should have. They established standards for behavior also. This is where the popular culture of our society has been so influential in forming opinions of right and wrong, morality and even sexual tastes. Anyone addicted to late-late movies will recognize the modern continuation of the Vamp and Virgin syndrome. The movies are an excellent barometer of where the country was at concerning women and sexual pleasure. Hollywood set up its own censoring committee, the Hayes Office, for the ostensible purpose of insuring public decency. What it accomplished in effect was to draw hard lines between good and bad girls and even harder lines on the female/feminine role in society.

This was long before hard core was a household word. It was a time when sexual scenes were for the most part only hinted at. The long passionate kisses would always end in a fade, which would pick up—later. How confusing it was for young girls to figure out what it was that happened in between. But what came through to them loud and clear is that the women who gave in to her sexual desires or worse, the one who was brazen enough to go after them, ended up badly. She was usually brunette and she represented the Vamp. The blond represented the Virgin: sensitive, suffering, submissive—in a word, less interesting.

Down nostalgia alley, some examples of classical Vamp pix come to mind at once: Bette Davis, that wonderful bad girl in *Beyond the Forest*, lusts after and consummates (off-screen) an affair with David Brian. She dies in the end of a self-induced abortion! Bette strays toward pleasure again in *The Letter* and ends up committing suicide. Joan Crawford, another sultry brunette who loved to be bad, starts off half-crazed with passion in *Possessed* and ends up totally mad. Then in *Humoresque* she plays a rich, married society lady who craves John Garfield and ends up thrown into the sea.

Gene Tierney brazenly pursues Cornell Wilde in *Leave Her to Heaven* but even marriage to him will not justify her all-consuming, physical passion: she ends up poisoned. How about Barbara Stanwyck, posing in a blond wig but always the seething brunette, in *Double Indemnity* where she empassions Fred MacMurray into murdering her husband only to be done in by him herself in the last reel.

There were famous blond exceptions who played bad girl roles with gusto, but I maintain that they were brunette types at heart. One of the great goddesses of love was Jean Harlow, of course. Another, still going strong, is Marlene Dietrich. Marilyn Monroe was a genius in the genre and she played in a classic of the type called *Niagara*. Who can forget the half-girl, half-monster of desire she created, lusting around the falls after her lover and strangled finally by her husband, Joseph Cotton. Lana Turner was/is an incorrigible inamorata on and off the screen. Remember the way she groped Garfield in *The Postman Always Rings Twice?* They both die, their passion duly punished. In real life Lana had a boyfriend (said to be connected to the underworld) who had the habit of beating up on her. One day her teen-age daughter Cheryl came to her mother's protection with a butcher knife and killed the boyfriend quite dead. A novel by Harold Robbins on the subject followed and inevitably a film, starring Susan Hayward, called *Where Love Has Gone*. I don't think Lana ever got a royalty.

Of course as movies got more "frank," sexual problems were woven into the plots and discussed more openly. Women did complain about their husbands (god forbid lovers) as sexual partners but when the actual details were ironed out, it was very often the woman's fault by somehow turning her husband off by not being attractive enough or being too ballsy. And when it was the husband's fault, the problem was that he wasn't getting enough, meaning quantity not quality. Two movies with the sex tigress of the fifties and especially sixties, Elizabeth Taylor, are good examples of this: in *Cat on a Hot Tin Roof* she is desperately trying to get her husband Paul Newman to make love to her, and in *Who's Afraid of Virginia Woolf* her husband Richard Burton persists in making snide remarks instead of love. The question of female orgasm has *not been tackled yet* despite the sexual breakthrough in movies.

Speaking of breakthrough, we have to pause for a moment and deal with those ultra-frank films where everything hangs out (quite literally), the pornos. Porno pix, just as porno books before them, are very influential in formulating opinions, especially in the young, of what "great" sex should be like. They also pretend to reveal the true sexual identities of women, so safely guarded from public scrutiny until now. So when a young woman starts having an orgasm the second after she's been penetrated, the tendency is to think that is the way it really happens. It is just thrilling to watch those porno kittens come and come and come. Why, none of them ever had a problem in her life! Whether we see her as a virgin first being introduced to sex or as a full-grown experienced woman of the world of twenty-two (they rarely look older than that) all you have to do is to wave a hard penis at her and she's writhing in ecstasy. Two widely distributed pix true to form in this department star the former Ivory Soap girl, Marilyn Chambers: *The Girl Behind the Green Door* and *The Resurrection of Eve.*

I remember thinking as I saw my first few pornos, "Why can't I come that fast, what's wrong with me?" Later when I knew better I realized that porno pix, just like books, are male fantasies of great sex scenes, not female. Porno-style lovemaking, furious pounding with gigantic cocks, is not likely to make the average woman come at all, let alone that fast. If guys think the performance of porno studs is what good lovemaking is all about, no wonder there are so many inept lovers around. The truth is that these are women and women's bodies and reactions as men imagine them in wet dreams. A woman who comes the instant or moments after she has been penetrated is so rare that it is almost pure male wish-fulfillment. The guy doesn't have to work at it that way, he doesn't even have to know anything about women's bodies or sexual needs, in fact there are no needs other than a stiff prick.

This confirms male superiority even in the sexual act, doesn't it? First the woman is tantalized by those rippling muscles writer Micky Spillane described; that's about all the foreplay she's going to get. Once Mike starts hammering, it's come time at once. All of us, during our impressionable years, read the dirty books. The strong themes which emerged were that women required brute strength, physical and intellectual subjugation, bodily abuse if necessary, in order to feel love and pleasure. No one paid any attention to the heroine's desires and needs. She was a mere foil for the hero's fantasies. We have come to a complete turnaround on this in the last decade, thanks to what has been dubbed the Sexual Revolution.

SEXUAL REVOLUTION

What actually brought on the Sexual Revolution is hard to pin down. It was certainly a happy conjunction of many factors, not the least of which was the end of centuries of frustration at having to keep sex in the closet. However I do believe the advent of the Pill cleared the way for a giant step toward sexual equality. As women became more daring once the fear of pregnancy was gone, we were more ready to admit that, yes we did enjoy sex and we were ready to go out and look for it with or without marriage. And wow did we get a lot of encouragement from the guys on this!

Overnight a magazine called *Playboy* appeared and proved in copious detail, both in pictures and print, that chicks were getting really liberated and were happy and willing to put out, no strings attached. Those centerfolds showed off the voluptuous bodies of child-women between eighteen and twenty-two, all ready for action. The picture stories show them all gardening or playing touch (*sic*) football with their friends, cooking or sewing, sweet wholesome creatures waiting for the "right man" to come along. In the meantime, they were open to proposals for fun and games. These women were the same sexual objects as their predecessors in literature and movies. The big difference was that it was no longer just the bad girls who indulged in sex, but good wholesome girls, who didn't have to be punished in the end. In this sense *Playboy* was one of the pace-setters of the new sexuality.

The big But, was that the rules were still set by men. The "desirable, attractive, feminine" way for women to look, behave, or put out was decided by male image-makers. The Playboy girls took over as the stereotype for female beauty and desirability: young, full-breasted and buttocked, athletic, starry-eyed about meeting Mr. Right, and sexually available. Remember the saying used to be that a guy lost his respect for a girl who put out? Well, now the situation was completely reversed and guys had no respect for girls who didn't put out. There was never any stress on the intelligence of these braless lovelies. I won't go so far as to say that the subtext implied they were dumb, but they certainly didn't present an intellectual challenge. It was the insecure man's dream come true.

Revolutions, once they've been won, have to be worked out. There are no guarantees, and as we are finding out, we may have the freedom to go after what we want, but nobody is bringing it around in a truck. The woman who wants to fulfill her sexual potential without marriage is going to run into a lot of trouble. She will encounter the hostility and resentment of establishment men and women. At least three times in my life a kind, attentive lover has turned into an enraged, insult-slinging boor because I declined the greatest tribute of all, a proposal of marriage, opting to keep my freedom to play the field. The new sexuality for women did not change the fundamental premise concerning what every decent, honest woman's desire should be—marriage!

Before the Pill, when sex was still called bad, the way girls justified themselves was by saying they were in love, the big L. They even believed it themselves. And being in love meant that you were hoping, or if you were lucky, planning to be married as soon as possible. And the boys believed it, too. I don't mean to make them all out as opportunistic rogues, they were caught in the guilt of sex and fear of pregnancy as much as we were. Everyone paid, it's just that women paid more. Insofar as women allowed, and I maintain, still allow, themselves to be manipulated by standards of beauty and behavior that are determined by a male-directed society, we women will continue to pay.

Let's take the case of a typical pre-Pill couple, Bob and Harriet. They meet, fall in love, go steady when they are both seventeen. By eighteen they are both in college and have become lovers. They keep this a big secret from their families, of course, because Harriet has lost her virginity and acted in a way her family would find reprehensible. She feels very guilty but has justified everything by "falling in love" and planning to be married. Bob feels guilty too, after all he has talked Harriet into "going all the way" and feels a responsibility toward her. She's expecting marriage and since they are in love, isn't that what life is all about? What about sexual compatibility? They don't have much basis for comparison but true satisfaction is supposed to come with the comfort and security of marriage, and that's the way they go.

As soon as the children come and their sex life has become infrequent and dull, Bob starts playing around. He suddenly discovers that he's fatally attracted to a female type diametrically opposed to Harriet and he wants out. She is crushed, not understanding what all the fuss about sex is about. She did her best to be a good wife in that department. But not having discovered sexual satisfaction with Bob, her only partner, she cannot understand the power of sexual passion. After her divorce when she started having her own career along with varied sexual experiences and discovered her own sexual needs and pleasures, she felt differently.

"I discovered I was sexy," she told me. "I never realized how sexually dissatisfied I was. I had no lover to compare my husband to or any real knowledge of my own needs. I could have spent the rest of my life never knowing real pleasure if Bob hadn't wanted to divorce. I still confuse sexual desire with love and secretly hope to remarry, but I'm first and foremost going to demand that a man makes me happy in bed before I even consider marrying him."

Here we are, all sexually liberated, career-oriented, having a good old time with one thought buzzing in our brains constantly, the name of the game is marriage. It used to be that if you chose carefully and put out judiciously, you could get your man. But coming across in the sack isn't going to single out any one of us any more because everybody's doing it. I will never forget the reactions I would get from fellows in the sixties when I didn't feel like jumping in the hay. It was like a fever and going to a party was like the old joke:

He: Hi.

She: Hi.

He: Have you read any good books lately?

She: Well, as a matter of . . .

He: Swell. Would you like to fuck?

Upon saying no, for whatever reason, I would hear

things like "Aren't you liberated, honey?" or "What're you, frigid?" or the classic "Oh, you dig chicks, eh?" We all heard those cracks and we all felt the same anger and humiliation at being exposed to the meat rack aspect of sexuality. While this permissive climate did allow women to express their sexual desires more openly with less guilt there was still not much attention being paid to female orgasm.

THE BIG LIE

Even today the competition for men goes on, and once you're over thirty, the going gets rougher. We still feel compelled to flatter a man's ego and while we're not afraid to stand up and speak out for what we believe in on the subjects of politics, religion, and such, we're still not demanding our rights in the sack. The first and most important of our inalienable rights is the one to orgasm. If we cannot insist on this with our partners and ourselves, we are not liberated at all. We have always been kept more or less in the dark concerning female orgasm even in the books intended to prepare women for marriage.

Did you know that most sex and marriage guides didn't even mention the female orgasm until the sixties? The guides were geared to teaching women how to *give* sexual satisfaction, not *receive* it. Words like climax and ejaculation described male pleasure peaks; euphemisms like *coital culmination* vaguely hinted that there might be something in it for both parties! The underlying contention was that men's sexual drives and needs for release far surpassed ours and therefore our main purpose was to keep them satisfied in this area. Today we know differently: women's capacity for sexual expression and satisfaction is equal or greater.

In our haste to compete with each other for men's approval and admiration, we began pretending we were getting more out of sex than we really were. We began lying about having orgasms. I have a crafty little French friend who's got her beret set on a guy and she'll get him to the altar as sure as she knows how to stew a rabbit. The fact that she doesn't have an orgasm with him is a mere detail. "Oo la, la, that ees not theee eemportant theeng, ma chérie. I can doo myself eether beefore or ahfter." When I asked her why she just didn't tell him instead of going through the sham of pretended orgasm, she answered that she didn't want to risk hurting his feelings and of course, losing him.

My friend was faking and lying in order to flatter her lover's ego. But once she's married and the years without orgasm accumulate and the pretending gets tedious and her frustrations mount—what then? Women are just beginning to come out of the closet concerning this subject, but from what information has already been collected, the degree and extent of faking orgasm is colossal. The girl who says to her new lover their very first time in the sack, "Oh it's never been so good," after moaning her way through pretended orgasm is obviously doing it to flatter him. At the same time she is giving him the impression that she is a very passionate girl so he is doubly impressed with his performance.

Another reason a woman lies is when she is too tired or doesn't feel like doing it in the first place. She will beg "faster, harder," pretending to like it better that way. In truth, she wants it over more quickly so she can go to sleep. But why shouldn't her lover end up thinking that is the way she really does like it and keep doing it like that all the time? He's not going to get better, she's not coming any closer to being more interested in sex. The vicious circle continues.

How many of us have lied and how many of us go on lying either to catch or to keep a man? If we truly believe in sexual freedom and liberation, we must start being honest with ourselves and our men. Lying about orgasm is an insidious trap because while it accomplishes the original purpose of flattery, there is no way of setting things right afterward. You wind up hating yourself for having lied and hating your man for leaving you high and dry. But even if a woman wants to tell her guy right from the start what her sexual needs are in order to reach orgasm, *she has to know them first.*

Women have to learn orgasm for themselves. It does not just happen automatically. Waiting for the magic lover to come along to make it happen is a cop-out first and a waste of time ultimately. Furthermore it is putting a burden on a man he cannot possibly cope with. Every woman is different with a different sense of timing that changes from love session to love session and again with each partner. She must tune into her own body and then make her lover of the moment know what to do at the moment she needs it.

The truth is that women can expand their sexual abilities to include more and better orgasms. For that we must know about the tricks and techniques required and feel free to experiment with them. Then we have to let our guys in on the game. There is no point continuing to be condescending to men by letting each one think he's the best lover we've had if he's not. Men will never get any better if we don't help them and neither will we if we don't find out about ourselves. Besides, there's something about the way resentments and frustrations keep popping back that makes the pretense hard to keep up. Think of it this way: it's an exciting game, learning the rules can be fun, and there's a prize at the end for everybody.

This book will give you all the important things you need to know: What the difference is between clitoral and vaginal orgasm. Where orgasm happens and how. What muscles are involved and how to strengthen them and control them. How to adapt lovemaking techniques for a more orgasmic climate. How to change the language of lovemaking from sexual which involves genitals to sensual which involves people. How to deal with problems like lubrication, menstruation, or menopause. How to avoid performance anxiety.

I once had a lover who was a well-known Don Juan. His lovemaking was very flashy, lots of swiftly-changing positions, much deep thrusting calculated to sweep you off your feet or off the bed. The final result was that it was too much like gymnastics for me and exhausting for both of us. After we got comfortable with each other I made a decision. One night after his big number I said, "Okay, that was round one and you took it. How about trying it my way this time?"

In a bemused but willing way he said, "Why not?" A couple of hours and several orgasms later he exclaimed, "This is fantastic. Why didn't you show me this before?" If you're curious about what I showed him and why he was so pleased, the following pages will reveal everything you want to know.

CHAPTER ONE

ANATOMY OF THE FEMALE ORGASM

SCENE: Dimly lit bedroom of Super Stud's bachelor pad. I'm lying on his fur spread, jumping out of my naked skin with anticipation. I want to touch his tanned health-club muscles, feel his eyelids flutter under my fingers, tantalize his ears and nape with butterfly kisses. I'm longing to have his palms discover the small of my back, alight on my buttock softly, make their way gently to my sensitive feet, thus setting me on fire.

But none of this is to be. A tongue two feet long whips around my tonsils while iron fingers probe my furry lips until the magic button is found. As I gasp for air, my cringing clit being rubbed to near extinction, I push and struggle. Ah, he thinks I'm going to resist a little to make the game more interesting. Rising to the challenge, SS wrenches my knees apart and thrusts his throbbing rod into my reluctant vagina. The fact that I am dry and tight is no deterrent to SS, who hammers away, crushing me with the full weight of his athlete's frame. The next few moments of crash-banging which seem like an eternity finally come to an end with much contented moaning from SS. "Ah, you're the greatest," he says to me, but he's really admiring what he is convinced is yet another astounding performance on his part. I gnash my teeth, and get the urge to kill.

The scene just described has been exaggerated ever so slightly for the purposes of humor. However I and many women I've talked to have had experiences that were similar. Furthermore if one is at all influenced by porno pix or books and even many sex how-to books, one could think that this is an erotic, exciting situation which should bring both parties to satisfaction. The truth is that with possibly few exceptions, this type of lovemaking is anti-erotic and thus anti-orgasmic to women. A basic knowledge of how women's bodies work and how climax is actually triggered is required to understand why this style of lovemaking is contrary to women's needs.

I want to examine what actually happens to our bodies, especially our genitals, during lovemaking and orgasm. I also want to explore the controversy concerning "clitoral" as opposed to "vaginal" orgasms because I feel many of us have been confused. It's all very well and good to be told ad nauseam that if: we have the right attitude toward sex, we learn how to relax, we lose our natural (?) shyness and inhibitions, sexual satisfaction will be ours. The inference here is that psychological factors are all-determining. The opposite school stresses physical technique till things get so mechanical, you feel like you've become part of a human erector set.

It is easy to understand why so much attention was

given to the importance of continual stimulation to the vulvar area, so rich in nerve endings, so quick to produce immediate reaction. And in this area, the teacher's pet popped up instantly, that most wondrous of nature's inventions which I sometimes refer to as the panic button—the clitoris. The word itself has always made me smile since it sounds as though it should be the name of a Greek movie star ... Clitoris Camamis, starring in *Never On Sunday.* Joking aside, its origin is Greek from *kleitoris* which means to close or shut up. The prepuce or hood of the clitoris swells during excitement and closes up over the sensitive organ to *protect* it from painful, direct contact during intercourse. There are more charming names, however, in all languages. In ours, button, rosebud, fucking fuse, and cherrystone are but a few. The French call it *le bouton* which means button, of course, but also means flower bud.

The beginnings of the controversy concerning clitoral and vaginal orgasms can be traced to Freud. He made distinctions between infantile and adult sexual responses, calling the need for clitoral stimulation (such as masturbation) to achieve orgasm a throwback to childhood. He maintained that the mature woman could and should achieve orgasm vaginally from the loving thrusts of the male member. Understandably this caused a great deal of consternation and confusion among the ranks of women getting a whole lot of fun out of masturbation by themselves or their partners, before, during and instead of intercourse.

It took a long time for women to break free of that no-no, especially girls like me who happen to think that masturbation is on occasion a very relaxing and rewarding nightcap (how many fantasies can you work up with a hot toddy, after all?). Men too felt insecure when a woman desired masturbation even though it was quite natural for men to require it in order to maintain or bring back erections. How many of us have had the experience where he says, "What's the matter, baby, aren't I enough for you?" or even worse, "Oh, so that's your hang-up, eh?"

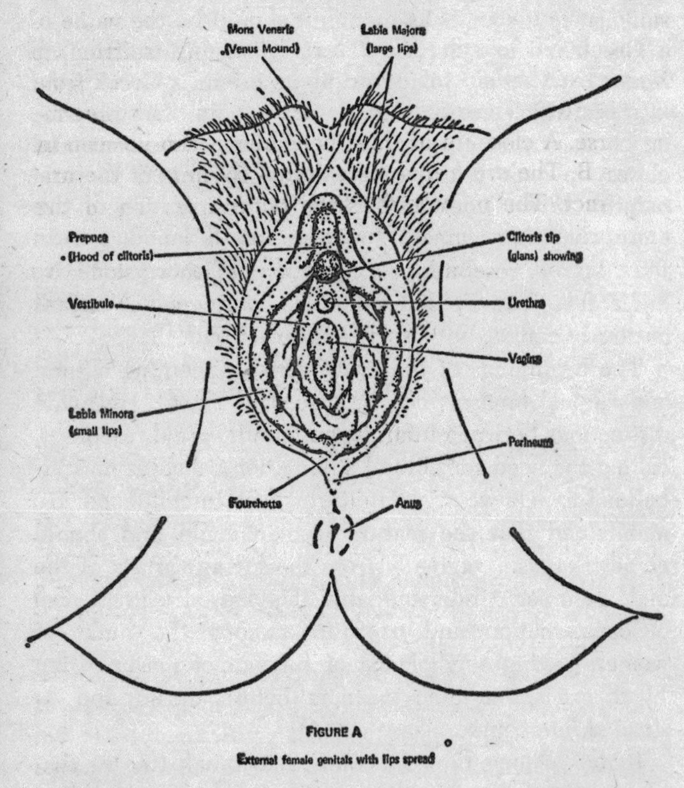

FIGURE A

External female genitals with lips spread

The make-up of the external female genitalia known as the vulva (and *not* the vagina, which is the internal birth canal) can be seen in Figure A. The *mons veneris* or Venus mound is the slightly pudgy area directly above the pubic bone and is covered with pubic hair. It is pudgy and hairy in order to bumper the bodies as the pubic bones rub against each other. Devilishly clever, don't you think? The *labia majora* or large, outer lips are covered with pubic hair also and likewise act as protectors for the more sensitive inner areas. The *labia minora* or small, inner lips, encompass the upper portion of the *prepuce* or hood of the clitoris.

This hood, like the inner lips, becomes very swollen during excitement and covers the sensitive *clitoris glans* or head from irritation during the forceful contact of intercourse. A close-up of this phenomenon can be seen in Figure B. The *urethra* is the external opening of the urinary tract. The *fourchette* is the bottom portion of the labia minora; it becomes very swollen during excitement and distends sometimes several inches, actually lengthening the vagina and wrapping around the penis at the same time. The *perineum* is the area between the vulva and the anus under which sensitive nerve ends lie. The *anus* is directly under this and is also very sensitive to stimulation.

Let's proceed to a close look at what an orgasm actually is, so that we can see what the roles of the vagina and the clitoris really are before attempting to give top billing. First of all I want to point out that an orgasm is not a mystical experience. It is a physical experience and can and has been recorded as such. Our responses go something like the following:

PHASE I: "Get Ready"—Our first reaction to sexual stimulus, the one that corresponds to the male erection, is lubrication of the vaginal walls. This can happen in ten seconds. Where this fluid comes from and how it seeps into the vagina through the walls, is still nature's mystery. The current theory is that as the blood rushes into the tissues making them get thick (engorgement is another word for tumescence), the tissues are squeezed together and fluid is seeped out causing a kind of

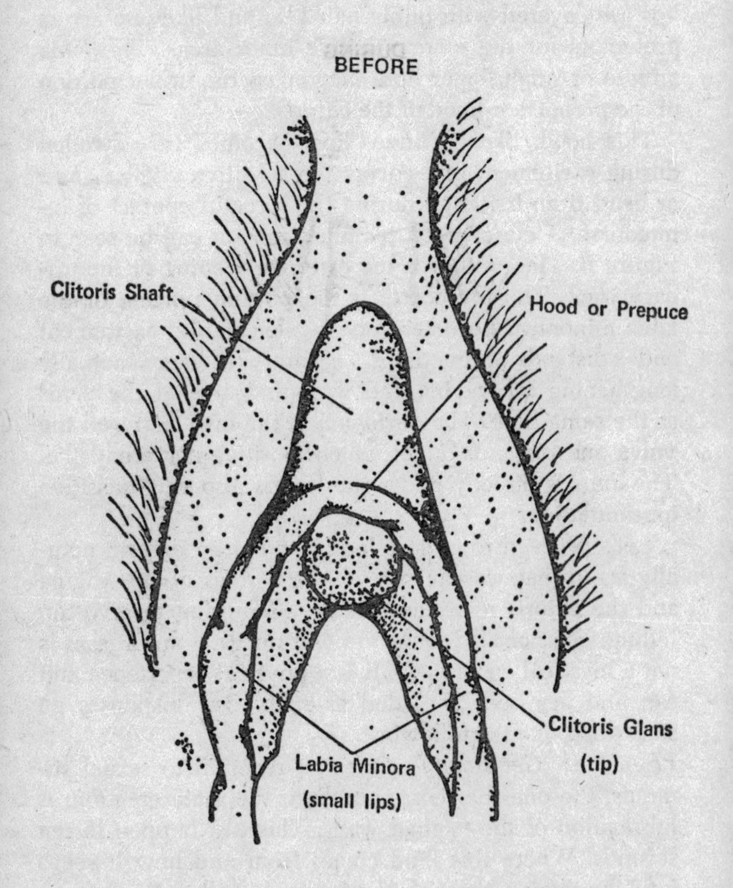
BEFORE
Clitoris Shaft
Hood or Prepuce
Clitoris Glans
(tip)
Labia Minora
(small lips)

DURING

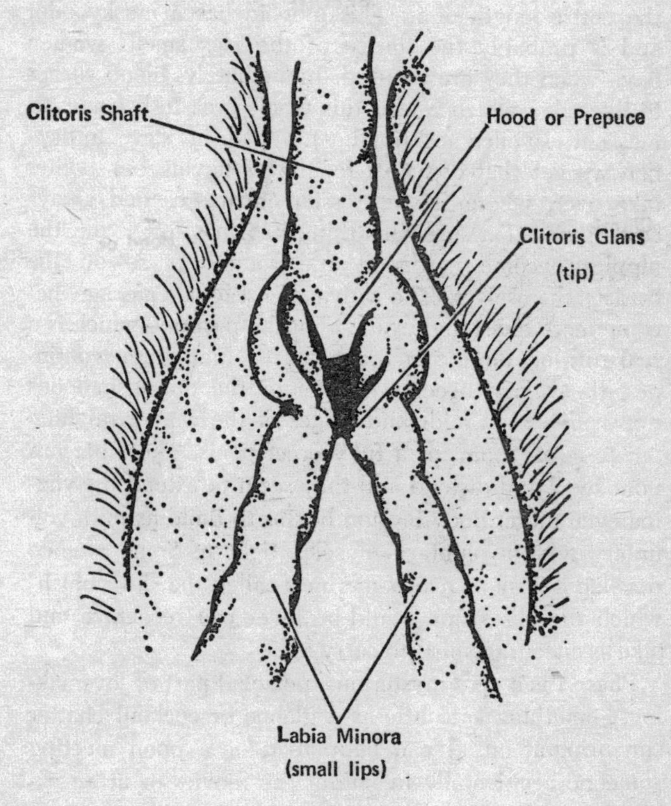

FIGURE B

Clitoris before and during sexual excitement

sweating. The Bartholin glands, located at the entrance to the vagina on either side, were thought to produce vaginal lubrication but they don't. What they do produce is a mucoid material which helps in penetration of the entrance to the vagina, and has nothing to do with the entire length of it. This mucoid has a musky odor and is probably the source of the "sex smell" women have when they are aroused. Immediately, blood rushes to the vulva which causes this whole area to become tumescent (swollen and tingling). When this starts to happen we get that delicious feeling of having our bodies take over, where the expression "being carried away" comes from, I'm sure. Breathing becomes faster and the nipples become hardened and sometimes so do the breasts themselves. The vulva and vaginal passage become more moist and exude a musky perfume which is a real turn-on for the connoisseur. As lubrication continues, the vagina becomes longer as the uterus balloons upward and the folds and ridges of the walls straighten out to make room for a fully erect penis. The labia minora swell and distend and they seem to extend the vagina even more. Body tension begins to build as both voluntary and involuntary muscles tighten. Some women develop a flush or rash sometimes called the "love blush" which the observant would-be lover can recognize and take as encouragement to carry on.

Phase I is a very mysterious, personal part of lovemaking. Something as subtle as a glance or cocktail chatter can bring it on. It can happen at once upon meeting someone accidentally in line at the movies or at an exhibition. Or it can happen suddenly with someone you've known for some time but never thought of in "that way." It is generally known as "being attracted" to another person, the attraction idea coming from the notion of an electro-magnetic pull between two poles.

And that's exactly how it feels, as we all know, like an irresistible pull toward another body.

With someone new, the thrill of surprise, the desire for discovery, speed up the attraction, and the bodily changes that come about can take place quickly. However with a regular lover when habit and perhaps a tiny bit of monotony have crept in, foreplay, including caressing, kissing, and any other extras that turn you on, is highly recommended. I like candles and incense myself and partial nudity. Sometimes merely a change of room or time can make a difference. Just remember that this first stage is absolutely essential to preparing the way for total satisfaction for a woman. A man can dispense with it entirely; a simple erection is all he requires to be ready. So see to it that Phase I takes place so that you can abandon yourself completely to the delights that should follow.

PHASE II: "Get Together"—With all the preliminaries delightfully underway, the hot, tingling sensation of your vulva and the moist longing in your vagina, the probings and entrance of a hot, hard penis feels like heaven. The adept lover will begin this phase very slowly and deliberately so that the sensations you feel can be very distinct and not blurred.

During the transports of actual intercourse, the changes increase rapidly. Breathing is of course much faster and the heartbeat has quickened. The swelling of the vulva has made it pudgy, and swelling in the vagina has narrowed the tunnel to half its normal width in order to grip the penis firmly. The clitoris elevates both in size (as the erectile tissue in the penis does) and in actual location. As the inner lips become thicker, they tend to pull the shaft and hood covering the clitoris down, half covering it.

Therefore contrary to popular misconception the clitoris is not *more* exposed during excitement, but less. It is easier to detect because it is swollen and therefore bigger, but it is covered. This is because of its acute sensitivity during tumescence. Men often feel the more they rub it the more they will excite their partners. Actually direct and prolonged stimulation is irritating and could have a positive turning-off effect, so don't be afraid to tell your partner to go easy.

By now the vaginal area has turned from pink to red and the tingling has turned to tension. While the muscles and the body in general build up some tension during Phase I, here instead of being diffused throughout, tension concentrates in the genital region. That's why we feel all "hot and bothered" down there. Concentration and regularity of rhythm and movement is extremely important for women during this stage of excitement. Women's tension builds up slower and is more easily upset than men's. That's why a cross word or a clumsy movement can be enough to break her tension build-up. When this happens, you know it because you can almost feel yourself drying up. Should it happen, the best thing is not to forge ahead with dogged determination but to wait a while until the "mood" returns. It is important to explain this to your partner because otherwise he will think you're just punishing him by not picking up again at once. Try to control your frustration since it will only get in everyone's way. After you're back in the saddle and your tension concentration is close to boiling again, the delicious delivery is the next fabulous phase.

PHASE III: "Getting Off"—All the tension will come together in a peak of release, a kind of huge sexual sneeze. We all differ on which area of the body first heralds the spasms. With some it's the top of the head, with me it's the toes. Men often say it starts as a hot wave across their shoulders. Wherever it starts, it makes its way to the vulvar and vaginal regions and creates the pleasure spasms we feel inside the whole abdominal area. These spasms last usually a few seconds but for most of us they seem like an eternity. The relativity of time is no where else better illustrated. The rhythmic muscular contractions of the vagina go right up to the uterus and this contracts also, although we're not aware of it. The exquisite convulsion can be observed in the facial expression of any woman not afraid to "let herself go" and is the most flattering grimace a lover can receive.

Here I must blast another popular misbelief concerning the "female ejaculation" (a common occurrence in porno literature). There is no such thing unless a woman's lubricating system is overactive. If it is and if she does "discharge" this lubricating fluid in one flush during the spasms, she is definitely a rare case. And besides the poor girl probably has problems since her vagina cannot have the same grip when it is over-lubricated. And now to the aftermath.

But first I have to pause here to tell you a joke, which I believe is appropriate. A movie star is exchanging confidences with a starlet in her dressing room between takes. She asks "Do you smoke after you come?" The starlet looks puzzled and then replies brightly, "I don't know but next time I'll have a look."

PHASE IV: "Relaxation"—While we don't smoke, we do simmer down. The tumescence of the labia, the vaginal walls, the clitoris, and the nipples subsides. The love blush disappears and the vagina moves back into its folds and ridges allowing the uterus to slide down to its normal position. It takes us a lot longer to go back to the "normal" state than it does men. This is why we welcome cuddling and mild caressing after lovemaking.

CHAPTER TWO

THE VAGINAL VERSUS CLITORAL CONFLICT

SCENE: Louise had made the astounding discovery that her lover not only did not mind her masturbating during lovemaking but it actually turned him on. She realized she must have had lingering guilt feelings about caressing herself because she had always been reluctant to do it with a lover. However now that she and John were "into" this new scene she felt free to explore the pleasures of simultaneously caressing her clitoris while John's penis moved inside her.

Of course positions had to be found which were comfortable to both, and the one she favored was lying slightly on her right hip with John entering her from behind, her left hip and buttock resting against his pelvis with her left leg lying over his left hip. This spread her legs, allowed her to get at her clitoral region, and allowed John to move freely *but* somewhat slower than usual since he was lying on his right side, and could not use hands, or feet, or knees to push with. One night after having had a few clitoral orgasms in this leisurely fashion, she sensed something different happening.

The tension in her vagina was growing with each clitoral orgasm rather than subsiding. She felt a need to continue rather than to stop. She asked John to keep up his steady, unhurried stroking because something was happening. John felt her body grow taut and as he caressed her nipples with his hands and nibbled at her ear she began to make noises she had never made before. Her caressing came to an abrupt halt with a delighted little scream: "I'm coming." She had had her first "vaginal" orgasm and naturally they were both surprised and thrilled.

Louise had had orgasm before and was quite convinced that "that was all there was" but when this happened, she knew it was different. Her caressing of her clitoris accompanied by John's leisurely stroking had triggered deep-seated vaginal spasms that brought about not only pleasure but a special kind of intense *release* which gave another dimension to her climax.

The research into where female orgasm really takes place and what triggers it is a fairly recent thing. The first steps toward conducting wide-range interviews and recording laboratory experiences began with Kinsey's monumental work and culminated in the publication of the Kinsey reports on males in 1948 and females in 1953. The news was out—practically everybody likes to make some kind of love. And even more astounding—that included women. Furthermore we were all equipped by nature or whoever with areas all over our body able to experience pleasure and it appeared that women were endowed with something special! Women have a clitoris whose *sole* function is to give pleasure. It is the only organ of the body that has no other purpose. A whole lot of people were fascinated and flabbergasted.

Masters and Johnson picked up where Kinsey left off and came up with other news. Almost all women could have orgasms by masturbating themselves, and women, unlike men, could have multiple orgasms in rapid succession. The concentration of very sensitive nerve endings of the clitoris compared to nothing else. Furthermore the vagina, except for the first third or thereabouts, seemed to have no nerve endings at all. Many women who participated in the experiments were hardly aware that they were being touched when the back two-thirds of their vaginas was probed.

Also discovered was the interconnection of the sensitive nerve networks of the pubic area, including the clitoris of course and the entrance to the vagina for that first third of the way. Another important discovery was that however it was brought about, by masturbation, intercourse, or dirty movies, the spasms that made up orgasm were the same. Masters and Johnson were categoric on this point:

> **From an anatomic point of view, there is absolutely no difference in the response of the pelvic viscera to effective sexual stimulation, regardless of whether stimulation occurs as a result of clitoral area manipulation, natural or artificial coition.***

Women were pretty glad to be able to read the results of thousands and thousands of case histories and experiments and discover what they all had in common. And women were pretty mad about having had to swallow the official line (as started by Freud) that masturbating was infantile and that if they didn't get an orgasm from penis-vaginal intercourse alone they were sexually im-

---

**Western Journal Of Surgery, Gynecology and Obstetrics*, 1962.

mature and needed help. (It is amazing how many more sophisticated doctors and analysts later went along unquestioningly with this line.) The confusion stirred up a lot of heated reactions.

When the women's liberation forces began to have some clout in the late sixties, things came to a head, so to speak. Anxious to help women claim an independent right to pleasure and slough off their sexual as well as other servitudes to men, strong voices in the movement jumped on the new evidence that vaginal orgasm was a myth and clitoral caressing is what orgasm is all about. Anne Koedt, in *The Myth of the Vaginal Orgasm*, wrote:

> **The establishment of clitoral orgasm as fact would threaten the heterosexual institution. The oppressor always fears the unity of the oppressed and the escape of women from the psychological hold men now maintain.**

This was tempered by other feminists, however. A good example is what Germaine Greer had to say in *The Female Eunuch* about clitoral orgasm and banishing men from the total proceedings:

> **A clitoral orgasm with a full cunt is nicer than a clitoral orgasm with an empty one, as far as I can tell at least. Besides a man is more than a dildo.**

With the news of the uniqueness of the clitoris and the fact that women have been happily spending long private hours caressing themselves to climax, information and directions on how to please women via the clitoris sifted down to the popular sex books. Husbands and would-be lovers were advised ad nauseam to keep the clitoris uppermost in their lovemaking techniques if they wanted to bring their women to satisfaction. They learned that this first and foremost step was an absolute must to getting a woman ready; that without it important things such as lubrication and dilation would not take place. Again women reacted strongly, saying they would not allow the clitoris to be appropriated by men as a means to their ends. It was an end in and by itself:

> **Women's orgasms are the result of the "right touches on the button." Sexologists are to be condemned for recommending stimulation of the clitoris merely as part of the prelude to intercourse, which most men consider to be the "real thing." What is in fact the real thing for them is *completely devoid of sensation* for the woman.***

The result of this was that the clitoris got top billing to the obvious neglect of the vagina. What's more, women had to put up with an awful lot of rough rubbing before they could work up the courage to say "take it easy." The clitoris is very delicate as every woman knows and can be caressed to discomfort very easily. This is the reason it has a hood, to protect it from direct rough contact *during lovemaking*, not to mention during manual stroking. This is the other important Masters and Johnson finding—that during straight intercourse the penis pulls down on the inner lips with each entry stroke and this pulls the clitoris hood at the same time—meaning that the clitoris does get a certain amount of stimulation during vaginal-penis contact also. Germaine Greer talked about this too:

> **If the right chain reaction could happen, women might find that the clitoris was more directly involved in intercourse, and could be brought to climax by a less pompous and deliberate way than digital massage.**

So the question became whether there are two kinds of orgasms, one clitoral and the other vaginal. If there is just one, where does it happen and what triggers it off? The clitoris has as its sole purpose to provide pleasure.

---

*Mette Tiljersen, *I Accuse.*

The vagina's main functions are to carry the menstrual flow and provide the birth canal. It is sensitive to touch and pleasure-giving only in its first third. The logical conclusion would seem to be that the clitoris is where it's all at. The only problem to accepting this was that thousands and thousands of women stubbornly insist that they *felt* different things, sometimes in the clitoral/vulvar area and sometimes deep in the vagina—and sometimes both places at once. So things were not so simple.

Dr. John Huffman, a gynecologist at Northwestern University School of Medicine, did extensive studies with women who had undergone the surgical removal of the clitoris because of disease. The results of his findings were that women who experienced orgasm before surgery continued to experience it afterward. Following through on this lead, Ford and Beach in *Patterns of Sexual Behavior* published their findings on women in primitive cultures where the clitoris was removed during puberty rites or later. Women maintained their interest in sex even with their clitorises gone *at puberty*, which means well before intercourse even began. By the way, the reasons for this cruel practice vary.

In some tribes it is to celebrate the female child's entry into womanhood by removing the vestigial penis (which is what the clitoris was thought to be). In others it is a prelude to the marriage ceremony destined to eliminate any interest the woman might have in sex, thus insuring her everlasting fidelity to her husband! How's that for cutting off the nose to spite the face? There always seems to have been a reason for mutilating or otherwise hurting the female body throughout history. To my knowledge no tribe, however primitive, ever worried about the possible feminization of their young men to the point of removing their nipples as vestigial remains of the breasts. Circumcision can be argued for on hygienic grounds, but the clitoris. . . ! However I'm digressing.

In any case these research findings seemed to bear out the idea that there might be two kinds of female orgasm. There were certainly many women capable of climax through direct clitoral stimulation who were nevertheless failing to reach orgasm during intercourse. And there were just as many women insisting that they had orgasms during intercourse which they felt in the vagina and which were different from clitoral climaxes. Yet scientific experts insisted that they could find no sensory possibility in the vagina where pleasure could be felt. And laboratory experiments indicated that at close range (a camera inside an artificial penis recording the orgasmic pulsations in the vagina) it all looked alike whether induced through clitoral or vaginal manipulation.

Now I have never gone to see a sexologist as a patient, only as a researcher. But if anyone along the line had tried to explain to me that what I was feeling during what I call a clitoral climax was the same as what I call a vaginal orgasm, I would have protested very loudly. A lot of women did, insisting that what they felt vaginally was very different. That is probably why the concept of the vaginal orgasm was not abandoned completely.

Women doctors and sexologists have gone on record with their personal experiences. Hilda O'Hare* finds clitoral orgasm "more shallowly placed and . . . localized in the anterior wall of the vagina not far from the clitoris itself, (while the vaginal orgasm) produces a pronounced and prolonged tonic state of the deeper placed vaginal muscles . . ."

---

*"Vaginal versus Clitoral Orgasm," *International Journal of Sexology.*

Sylvia Payne† finds the "vaginal orgasm has a sucking characteristic . . . clitoral orgasm is a discharging orgasm . . . Joan Malleson, in *Any Wife or Any Husband*, on the one hand states that the clitoris is the source of the greatest sexual feeling for the majority of women; on the other hand she refers to the "external" clitoral orgasm as a pleasurable but less satisfying substitute for the "complete fulfillment" that comes with the "internal" vaginal orgasm.

Dr. Seymour Fisher, after conducting his own research and interviews, states in *The Female Orgasm*, "In any case, there seems to be reason to say that the so-called clitoral and vaginal orgasms, at least in their extreme forms, do differ experientially." He had come to the conclusion therefore that there must be a difference of quality of experience for many, many women. Even feminist Kate Millet in her *Sexual Politics* concludes: "While there is no 'vaginal orgasm' per se, there is of course orgasm in vaginal coitus (and probably one of a different experiential character than that produced by exclusively clitoral stimulation)."

Dr. Helen Singer Kaplan acknowledges both types of orgasm in her book *The New Sex Therapy*:

> **Current evidence suggests that stimulation of the clitoris is important and probably crucial to the production of the female orgasm. However when she is fully aroused and excited a woman may climax after only two coital thrusts by a beloved partner.**

At one point Masters and Johnson define the function of the clitoris as the "transmitter and conductor" of erotic sensation. It would seem then that the sensation has to be transmitted and conducted *somewhere*. Could it be that sensation begins in the clitoris and then when

---

†"A Concept of Femininity," *British Journal of Medicine and Psychology*.

conditions are right (psychologically as well as physiologically) they move up into the vagina where they explode into the deep-seated spasms women keep describing as vaginal orgasm? And when conditions are not right and the sensations which begin in the clitoral-vulvar area *stop* there—could that be what is described as clitoral orgasm?

Dr. Paul Popenoe of the American Institute of Family Relations says:

> **In discussions with thousands of women our counselors find the clitoral orgasm is described as superficial, a nervous contraction which is not fully satisfying. The vaginal orgasm is described as being profound, seeming to involve the entire body in an explosive warmth and providing a very rich and deep release and satisfaction. It is clear however that a very great many women have rarely or never experienced such a climax.**

Herein lies the rub, as far as I can see. There are so many women who do not know what vaginal orgasm is (from the looks of it, two-thirds of all women tested) and yet are perfectly capable of experiencing clitoral orgasm at once through their own caressing. Naturally the tendency would be to think, or hope, that "that's all there is." Dr. Philip Polatin of Columbia University does not think so: "A woman's sexual response differs from a man's because she has not one but two means of achieving orgasm and these two kinds of orgasm differ markedly from each other. Also both may occur simultaneously or one may follow the other. The first is what is known as the clitoral orgasm, induced by stimulation of the clitoris, (some women do not know any other type of orgasm . . .) a prolonged excitation resulting in a sharp climax. Then there is the vaginal orgasm, experienced deep within the vagina."

It is certainly true that women capable of pleasure are deeply moved by the entrance of the penis, that they become deeply stimulated by intercourse itself, and that some, at times, can reach orgasm without much, if any, external stimulation. Dr. Kaplan states that she does not think conclusive scientific evidence has been collected up to now to disqualify the possibility of dual orgasm. And Dr. Fisher suggests that Masters and Johnson "may have underestimated the amount of nonclitoral arousal produced by vaginal stimulation in its own right via its kinesthetic effects (for example, sense of vaginal and muscle stretching). The written comments of women concerning their experiences during vaginal intercourse leave little doubt that they perceive it and 'feel' it as more than just a variant of clitoral arousal."

Exactly what is it that all these women feel? Where are these vaginal sensations expressed? And how can there be any sensation at all if the vaginal walls are lined with tissue resembling that of the intestine which contains no nerve endings to speak of? Yet other women, most women perhaps, do not feel these sensations or feel them only vaguely. Why is this?

The answer to these questions was discovered by mistake, but it can give women the means with which to assert their birthright not only to sexual equality but to total satisfaction as well. I call it the PC factor.

CHAPTER THREE

THE PC FACTOR

SCENE: Dorothy was distressed and embarrassed. She had just had her third baby and was delighted at having put childbearing behind her for good. She and her husband had gotten back to their normal pace of lovemaking and it seemed duller to her than ever before. But that wasn't the problem. She had never laid great store in physical love and accepted very cheerfully the fact that Jim needed more sex and got more out of it than she did. But she used to feel—something—and now even that was gone.

But the *real* problem was what her doctor called urinary incontinence. One out of every twenty women in America has it. A sudden cough, a laughing bout, a bump in the car, would cause her bladder to release a little urine, just enough to leave a wet tell-tale circle on the back of her skirt or pants. Her doctor sent her to a specialist and he advised against surgery since it rarely helps. He did teach her exercises which were designed to strengthen the muscles controlling the sphincter of her urethra. She did them religiously and when she returned to see the doctor six weeks later she was radiant.

"Ah, I see the exercises worked," he said. She threw her arms around his neck and kissed him, "Did they ever! I've been having orgasms for the first time in my life."

This little story is typical of the experiences of many women who were treated with great attention and care for bladder dysfunction, not orgasmic dysfunction! But let me tell you how it all happened. Dr. Arnold H. Kegel, a specialist in women's disorders, was not satisfied with the result of surgical treatment for urinary incontinence. Even when surgery succeeded, the results might be only temporary. He suspected that a weakened muscle was at fault, so he devised ways of strengthening that muscle to see if he was right. The muscle in question runs between the legs, from front to back, like a sling. It is wide and strong. In fact, it forms the floor of the pelvis, the lower trunk. It is the base of support for the bladder, part of the rectum, the vaginal canal, and the uterus. It is called the *pubococcygeus* (pronounced pyoo'bo kok sij'eus) because it runs from the pubis, the bone underneath the mons veneris which forms the tip of the pelvis, to the coccyx, the base of the spine. To make things simple, we'll call it the PC muscle.

Doctor Kegel's exercises have now become famous for the treatment of bladder control deficiency, but that's not all. When he began hearing more and more accounts like Dorothy's, he began to wonder about a possible connection between the urethra sphincter tightening and a vaginal spasm reaction. At first he was skeptical, but then he took a closer look at the pelvic floor muscles. (See Figure C.) They are composed of several layers. The outermost layer is made up mainly of sphincters, ring-like tightening and closing muscles. They keep shut the outer openings of the urinary passage, rectum, and vaginal canal. These are relatively weak muscles and can be stretched very easily (by childbirth, for instance).

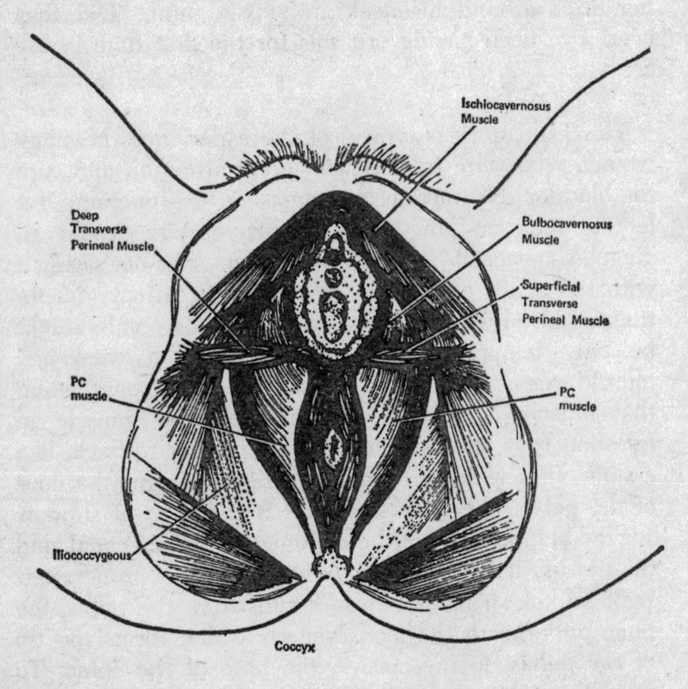

FIGURE C

However lying inside these outer muscle layers is a very thick (more than two inches), strong muscle, the PC. Imagine the three canals, bladder, vagina, rectum, passing through the muscular floor. Each canal's passage is surrounded by a net of interlocking muscle fibers from the PC. The fibers run both lengthwise along each canal and surround each as sphincters. This way, the rings of muscle around each passage can be squeezed shut at will. It is the sphincter action of that part of the PC surrounding the urinary passage which fails in urinary incontinence; the PC cannot squeeze the passage shut. Exercise can give it back the strength to function properly.

What has this to do with vaginal response? Kegel knew first that the PC surrounds the vagina in the same way. Then upon closer examination of women in general, not just those with urinary problems, he discovered that a surprising number of women had PC weakness! In fact fewer than one out of three women had good PC muscle tone. For those women with good PC tone, childbirth was easier and the birth canal was rarely damaged during delivery. *And* vaginal responsiveness was high.

But for the two out of three women with poor PC tone, the muscle sagged something like a hammock and the organs it was meant to support sagged also. Among these women, childbirth was more likely to be difficult. Birth canal injuries were more common. Incontinence appeared after children were born and sometimes as early as their own childhoods. And sexual satisfaction, in the form of vaginal orgasm, was very unusual.

Now before I go any further in explaining how the PC works, I want to make an important point concerning these findings. These women who experienced little or no sensation in their vaginas once intercourse began were non-orgasmic in the vaginal sense only. Their clitorises were perfectly sensitive to stimulation, and they could experience clitoral spasms through masturbation, petting, and oral caresses. Many of them took these to be complete orgasm, meaning they thought, just as I did when I was a young woman, that "that's all there was." It was only when they started experiencing the vaginal type of orgasm did they realize the difference. I think there is no better evidence around that a difference does indeed exist.

The idea just may occur to some of you that the Kegel approach would seem to back up Freud's emphasis on vaginal rather than clitoral orgasm. I want to quickly point out why this is not the case. For Freud there is a change of libido from the clitoris to the vagina in the interest of femininity and psycho-sexual maturity. For Kegel the vaginal orgasm is simply a neuro-muscular conditioned reflex response based on intact and healthy vaginal muscles.

When the PC muscle is slack and has lost its resilience it means the woman has lost not only support for important organs, she has also lost the ability to squeeze these muscles around her sphincters. Why is the ability to exert squeezing pressure important? Doctors Terence McGuire and Richard Steinhilber of the Mayo Clinic explain: "According to current data, the muscle beneath the vaginal mucosa (lining of the vagina) are well supplied with proprioceptive endings (nerve endings sensitive to pressure, movement, and stretching). These are adequately stimulated during intercourse, and could well represent the primary sensory apparatus. It would appear that vaginal orgasm is a reality."

In other words, the muscle surrounding the vagina is rich in sensitive nerve endings. Doctors failed to find these endings because their search was limited to the *lining of the vagina.* Since these nerves are outside the vagina, it takes firm pressure from within to stimulate them. In a wide, slack vagina, the penis makes poor and infrequent contact with the walls of the passage, thereby stimulating the nerves in the surrounding muscles hardly at all.

How many of our young girls get taught the importance of vaginal muscular control in their high school sex-education classes? This is a rhetorical question calculated to make your blood boil! I defy any school in the country to come forth and say they offer such education. The very subject would make the school board blush, not to mention the instructors themselves. What's even more pitiful is that the parents would be right out front screaming that they didn't want their daughters instructed in the art of prostitution or some such nonsense. Because that is where the establishment's head is still at concerning sexual satisfaction for women.

In my so-called sex education class I became insistent that our teacher explain clearly how to tell a virgin from a non-virgin. You can imagine how important that question was to all of us during a time when we were yearning to experience sex and trying to keep our legs together at the same time in order to protect our precious reputations. The teacher became livid, called me a trouble-maker (which I was), and said she was giving us enough information for our ages, which was between fourteen and fifteen. Hah! A third of the girls were pregnant and needed abortions before their sixteenth birthday. And we're supposed to be civilized.

Many Oriental and primitive peoples without our hang-ups have long been aware of the need for muscular control and teach their young women accordingly. In one African tribe, no girl may marry until she proves (!) she has practiced her homework and can exert the proper muscular control. And we've all heard the sailors' tales about the Near-Eastern prostitutes who can hold a man prisoner in their vaginas a whole night long. That's a long time to contract, but I can see where it might be fun for the sailors. Other cultures have noted that sexual performance is poorer after childbirth because of the stretching or injuring of the birth canal. In some Moslem countries women actually go so far as to pack the vagina with rock salt after giving birth to make sure it contracts!

Further confirmation of vaginal orgasm comes from Dr. John Oliven of New York's Columbia Presbyterian Hospital. In a textbook for physicians and other professionals he says:

> **The most important hypesthesic (lack-of-feeling) syndrome occurs in connection with vaginal over-relaxation. To the patient herself this may appear to be a matter of insufficient contact between penis and vaginal walls. However there is evidence that relaxed walls are hypesthesic walls because the sub-mucosal "deep-touch" nerve endings which are responsible for the greater part of so-called vaginal sensation, are minimally represented if their vehicle—chiefly the pubococcygeus—is hypotrophic (weak through underdevelopment or degeneration). Thus, probably no degree of "bulk immission" (no matter how big the penis is) can completely overcome these women's diminished sensation.**

When I read this I remembered the sad experience of a friend of mine before sex therapy even existed. She was bouncing her six-month daughter on her knee and tears were rolling down her cheeks. "Jack and I used to have such fun in bed until I had the baby. I got all stretched and the doctor said it was because I got ripped when she was delivered. I went back especially so he could sew me up tighter. It hurt like hell and it didn't even help. Jack's got a normal-sized cock and anyway it was always big enough for me, but now . . . I hardly feel anything." I know now what her problem was, and tightening the entrance to her vagina was not going to solve it. It was the widened vaginal walls caused by the stretched PC muscles that were the trouble.

Good vaginal muscle control is something we can all have. By exercising voluntary muscles we can reinforce the whole area of the PC sling and produce the conditions of pressure and tension needed to *trigger the involuntary* spasms of vaginal orgasm. In a very famous sex manual written over forty years ago called *The Ideal*

Marriage, Van de Velde had already gleaned the importance of muscle control, but of course his main concern was male satisfaction: "The whole structure (of the female organs) accentuated by the working of the *muscles* is an apparatus for gripping and rubbing the male sexual organ, during and after its insertion into the vagina, and thus to produce the ejaculation of seed or sperm-cells, in the culmination of excitement, and at the same time, by pressure and friction, to ensure this orgasm, or some pleasure and ecstasy, in the woman *also*." Don't you just love that *also*?

Doctor Kegel started a clinic at USC's School of Medicine in 1948. His work won the annual award of the Los Angeles Obstetrical Society because PC tone helped in childbearing as well as curing urinary incontinence. At that very clinic countless numbers of women were sent to him by the American Institute of Family Relations because they suffered from vaginal inadequacy during sexual relations. Nobody made much of a fuss about them, however.

As long ago as the turn of the century, Dr. Robert Dickinson reported that he could identify women likely to fail sexually by examining them. "The size, power, reactions and rhythm of contraction of the pelvic floor muscles give information concerning vaginal types of coital orgasm (orgasm during intercourse)." Of one of his cases he wrote: "Levator (another way of referring to PC muscles) is not very good. Taught her to use the muscle." He adds, "It seems very important that many women are able after instruction to get something which they call orgasm, when they failed before instruction." *Seems very important* he said!

Not important enough to become tradition, however, because thousands of textbooks on sex, marriage guidance manuals, and articles have been written since then, the majority stressing male satisfaction, relegating female orgasm and how to achieve it (when it was mentioned at all) to secondary importance. And when female orgasm finally began to be talked about, they were busy trying to "prove" the vaginal orgasm was a myth!

Dr. Maxine Davis got angry, too, in *The Sexual Responsibility of Women:*

> **Psychiatrists have wasted endless hours of their own and their patients' time trying to probe into subconscious emotional factors in frigidity when all the patient needed was systematic exercise of her horrendously labeled "pubococcygeus muscles."**

What do they say about a rose by any other name? Medical names for things have never been very pretty but I do think the abbreviation to PC is somewhat better. Now what we really must do is make it an everyday word for every woman who is interested in exploring her threshold of pleasure.

With the discovery of the PC factor we know some very important basic truths that will help us to assert ourselves with confidence as far as vaginal orgasm is concerned. There are ways to find out how to rate your own PC factor. It may be your own gynecologist will not be able to tell you. The last time I saw my gynecologist I asked her to check my PC quality with her perineometer (an instrument devised to do just that). Her eyes widened. She obviously didn't know what I was talking about. When I explained, she was quite embarrassed and said that for "sexual problems" I would have to see a sexologist or go to a sex clinic. I said, "But what if I didn't know I even have a sex 'problem'? Aren't you the one, when you examine my vagina, to tell me I have one, if I do?" She got even more embarrassed. That's where a lot of gynecologists are at concerning the PC factor. Don't give up. Keep calling until you find one who knows. They exist.

In the meantime, there are a few tests you can conduct on yourself before running off to an expensive sex clinic. And there are exercises, the famous Kegel inventions, which can simply change and improve your enjoyment of sex beyond imagination. Believe me because I was orgasmic enough but decided to do them anyway, just to see. The result was an increase in the intensity of pleasure that was truly dynamite.

CHAPTER FOUR

THE SEX FLEX

SCENE: Adrienne knew what sex was all about. She knew every part of the male and female genitalia by heart and how each functioned to boot. Right from the beginning sex was clear sailing; her mind was wide open to all kinds of experimentation and her psyche uncluttered by guilt. She was acutely aware that the clitoris was the key to feminine response in lovemaking and she was on the best terms with hers, right from childhood in fact. She taught her lovers about her clitoris. Their attitudes ranged from cooperative to wildly enthusiastic when she caressed herself to climax during lovemaking. She took pride in being a highly orgasmic gal.

One day she saw an article in the *Eastern Sexual Science Quarterly* entitled: "Do You Have Clitoromania?" Out of curiosity she read on, knowing full well this was going to be another nonsense piece destined to impress ignorants. "Has your clitoris become a crutch?"

the article asked. "Are you settling for half the pleasure you could have by not developing your vaginal potential?" With that she really started to get interested. She learned about the PC factor and the muscles that controlled it. She discovered that these muscles could be worked voluntarily with special exercises called the Sex Flex. She studied the exercises and did them with the dedication of a saint. Two months later she came out of the clitoral closet. With a minimum amount of external stimulation she abandoned herself to her vagina and her lover. The results were dynamite. She experienced a vaginal orgasm, full, deep satisfaction, for the first time in her life. When it happened again, she was sure she had done her homework well, so she felt free to *add* the simultaneous self-caressing to her lover's contribution. Results: double dynamite. Oh, where had she been all those complacent years. Now she could have it both ways either separately or simultaneously. That's something that we women have over men in the sex-pleasure department. *Vive la différence!*

The first thing a woman should do is to check for the location of her PC muscle. There are a few ways of finding out where your PC is and what it feels like. Begin by contracting your whole vaginal and rectal region. Even that little bit of tightening should give you a tingle. Then tighten just the vaginal area. You will see that you can separate these. Then concentrate on tightening very deep inside your vagina, trying consciously to reach up to the muscles higher up rather than just the sphincter. Put a finger in your vagina as you do this tightening again. Keep it up until you feel your vagina "grip" your finger. Once that happens you have located your PC and will be able to proceed with the exercises.

Another way is to lie flat on your back with your knees raised and open with a good-sized mirror (not a compact mirror) reflecting your whole genital area. Contract your PC, remembering to reach deep inside for the continuation of the muscle. You will see the perineum (the area between the vaginal opening and the anus) rise. When it does you should feel the inner tingling I mentioned earlier. If you have doubts, see a savvy gynecologist; call first and make sure he or she knows what the PC is *and* possesses a perineometer (instrument to test PC).

Many women can contract the PC at will by merely finding out that it exists. In fact there are women who can get pleasure from vaginal intercourse for the first time by merely being made aware of the muscle and its role in sex. But if the PC is weak, and it is in two out of three women, awareness is not likely to be enough. Not only do you have to learn conscious control of the PC, you must also learn to strengthen it with exercise. The originator of the PC exercises, Dr. Arnold Kegel, says "It is a rare woman who cannot benefit from increased strength of the PC."

I should point something out here before we get into any confusion. The deep muscles of the vagina that produce orgasm are involuntary. But they are affected, stimulated, and strengthened by muscles immediately surrounding the vagina which can be controlled voluntarily. This does not mean that you can easily have a vaginal orgasm just by squeezing a few muscles. What it does mean is that by training the muscles you *can* control, you will reach the ones you can't and make them more responsive.

These are the contractions women frequently use to fake orgasms. We who have done this know how easily men can be tricked; they cannot feel the deeper, real thing. They feel only the contractions of the muscles immediately surrounding the vagina because these are the ones that grasp the penis. Only we can feel the real thing. However the very muscles we faked with can lead the way to new pleasure. By using the Sex Flex every day, we can strengthen both superficial and deep PC muscles into new vitality. Once the lazy PCs are activated and start producing orgasms, they acquire a kind of *muscle memory* and act on their own without having to be kicked off by deliberate contracting.

By the way, the muscle memory concept is something all athletes and people having done sports know about. Often people who skied a lot during younger years, go back to it after ten or so years of abstinence to discover they don't have to start from scratch. "It came right back to me," is the expression they often use. That means when the muscles were called upon to do a movement they hadn't done in years, a kind of reflex action developed and they got back into it. That may be the explanation of why women whose clitorises were removed surgically could still experience orgasm vaginally *if they were experiencing it before the surgery.* The PC muscles act reflexively just like any others.

The most conclusive way to test your PC control on your own is with your urine flow. The PC surrounds and controls the sphincter of the urethra and good PC control means good urine control. So wait until you have to urinate very badly. If while sitting on the toilet during a heavy, urgent flow, you can contract your muscles and stop or substantially slow down your urine stream, chances are you're in pretty good shape. However weaker, superficial sphincter muscles can sometimes substitute and do the job. So just to make the test conclusive, keep your knees apart when you're doing this experiment. Even if you don't succeed, which means you lack PC control, you will have learned (by experimenting with how to at least slow down the flow) where your PC is and what it feels like. With that you can proceed:

SEX FLEX EXERCISES

1. Begin by doing five or ten contractions before even getting out of bed. They will seem easier to you then. No one need know what's going on, it's your little secret.

2. Each time you empty your bladder, use your contractions just as you did in the first experiment. It's a great opportunity to exercise anyway. Control will get better each day and encourage you on.

3. Upon getting into bed at night, do another ten contractions. With this loose schedule as a guideline, you should be able to reach sixty contractions a day. They should take a second each to do and not fatigue you in the least. The day's total time spent in doing the PCs is exactly . . . one minute!

This program should be stepped up as the contractions become effortless for you. Increase them to 20 per session then 30 until you reach up to 250 or 300 a day at whatever times are most convenient for you. Just like abdominal isometrics, they can be done while sitting at the hairdressers or waiting for the bus. The difference is that they are easier and won't give your face a contorted look of strain.

Most sex clinic patients reach a total of about 300 a day by the end of six weeks. By this time a woman is usually able to control her urine flow easily. Most women report a difference in their vaginal perception after three weeks, but continuation to six weeks is urged. And six weeks is long enough. The PC's initial task is that of pelvic support and is normally in a state of partial contraction. Unless it were, bladder retention would not be possible at all. The PC relaxes completely only under anesthesia.

The exercises strengthen this steady state of contraction. Furthermore lovemaking actually helps preserve the new muscle tone in a number of ways. First, it seems as though the steady-state contraction is heightened during intercourse. Second, sexual stimulation seems to set off mild reflex contractions of the vaginal muscles. Third, many experts counsel women to make occasional conscious contractions as a technique of intercourse in order to develop the trigger-mechanism of the involuntary spasms. Finally when vaginal orgasm is achieved, the PC contracts involuntarily, strongly and rhythmically, supplying the PC and its mistress with the best exercise either of them can get.

One charming recommendation is offered to women about to embark on a PC training course for the purposes of vaginal awakening. While doing a session of contractions, try conjuring up your favorite sexual fantasies. Why not, it's a lovely way to spend time anyway. But for our purposes, it creates an association between lovemaking and contractions which should make them come more easily during the real thing.

The development of the PC's role in childbirth has long been normal procedure in obstetrics. Expectant mothers are often advised to do the Sex Flex (except it's not called that) since better PC tonus will make delivery easier and prevent possible damage to the muscle itself and the vaginal walls. Often doctors during deliveries have to make an episiotomy (cutting into the fourchette to keep the baby's head from ripping it, a clean cut makes stitching afterward that much easier). If this is done hurriedly or incorrectly for some other reason, the PC can be damaged. Women with good PC tone even after one child, will often lose it with second or third births. The Sex Flex is recommended after birth in order to restore PC tone and head off incontinence or other complications.

A doctor described an incident where a sixty-year-old female colleague in marriage counseling stopped in at one of his lectures on the sexual importance of the PC muscle. She asked questions, all in the spirit of cooperation, he thought. He did not see her again until a month later. She came running toward him, the whole length of a hospital corridor, threw her arms around his neck, and confessed that for the first time in forty years of marriage she had experienced a full orgasm.

There are two important points made by this very touching story: the first is that even among *women* professionals in the fields of female sexual function, the PC was ignored not only as the key to vaginal response, but as a factor at all. The second point is that age need not be an obstacle to developing better PC control and sexual response. That is great news for all older women.

CHAPTER FIVE

SLOW & EASY: THE CURE FOR RABBIT FEVER

SCENE: "Rabbit Fever" is my pet name for the "Wham Bam, Thank You Ma'm" style of loving. This maddening attitude toward lovemaking is usually attributed to traveling salesmen and truck drivers. But no category of male should be excluded. Once I met a well-known author whose literary reputation was equaled by his reputation as a womanizer. He had been divorced by three wives, and had a child by each. At the time of our scene, he had just separated from wife number 2.

"She walked out calling me the most egotistical man she had ever met." He was very upset and confessed he was trying very hard not to believe that all women were fickle, capricious, and not to be trusted. "One time we had just finished making love and it was wonderful, beautiful. I lay back, basking in pleasure when all of a sudden she jumped to her feet and started beating me with her fists, screaming 'you pig, you bastard!' I never found out why." He looked pained.

I felt very sorry for him and thought that he must have married a really uptight prude who just hated sex but wouldn't admit it. Eager to console him and convince him that all women didn't hate sex, I decided to accept his invitation to an enchanted weekend in the country.

The scenario of our lovemaking went something like this: The minute we got into the room and dropped our bags, there was some pretty fancy kissing and groping while edging toward the bed. My mind wandered to scenes I remembered from his books where the man contemplated the soul and psyche of the woman with such compassion and sensitivity, I thought, "At last a man who understands women." I hit the bed with a thump and in seconds the essentials were off and in one fast jam, without benefit of any kind of foreplay, he had rammed a monumental erection into me. I moaned with pain but he must have interpreted that as pleasure because before I had a chance to say "wait a minute," it was all over and he was showering.

The first, second, and third time around I was willing to make allowances for the excitement of the newness of our situation but, as the weekend progressed, it looked very much like a pattern had emerged. I found myself in the familiar, uncomfortable position of having to tell a man, "You're a swell guy but a lousy lover." Why couldn't he see that nothing was happening for me? I was constantly repeating "Take it easy. Slow down. Wait for me." Finally I said, "Look, uh, all this fast and furious action is a real turn-on but, uh, it's getting to be a bit frustrating as well . . . I'm not . . ." He interrupted, "Yes, I noticed you weren't quite with it. Sorry you have trouble having orgasms."

My jaw hit the floor. "I have no trouble at all, given a

decent amount of time and preparation. You come into me too fast, you pump away too hard, and you come too soon! That's the only trouble *I'm* having!" He looked indignant, "Don't get hostile, please. I've made love very successfully all my life and I don't need any lessons from you."

As you can imagine my enchanted weekend came to a screeching halt. I realized then why his wife had gone into a post-coital rage. A man with his attitude may be beyond help as his marital record suggested. However hope springs eternal since he recently married wife number 4. This man sincerely believes there's nothing wrong with his lovemaking because he is "doing what comes naturally." Besides all the stories, jokes, traditions, pornos, and the like would suggest that a constantly prodding ramrod is every girl's dream come true. The idea that lovemaking does not come naturally, that it is a technique that must be learned, is a new one, in the United States at least.

One evening, after a conversation concerning sex, an earnest young man asked me, "What is the right way . . . you know . . . the natural way, to make love?" I had to laugh at the naiveté of this question and yet it's not so funny since anthropologists, sociologists, and scientists have asked the same question and looked for the same answer all over the world. First of all, the "right" way, meaning the pleasurable way I presume, is not always the "natural" way, meaning a way society approves of. I think most specialists agree that practically no human being reaches an age of sexual ability without carrying a heavy load of taboos, fears, and misconceptions about the sexual act. If there ever was an instinctive way of making love for humans and surely there must have been some norm at some stage of evolution, it has been buried under multiple strata of society after society.

From early manuscripts, such as India's *Kama Sutra* dating from the third century A.D., we can see that the art and techniques of love are very sophisticated matters. These ancient documents were already very preoccupied with the sexual pleasures and satisfaction of the woman and in dedicated detail went into the endless variations involving the paths to pleasure through touch, taste, sight, and sound. "The individual tastes of a person are of much greater importance than the customs or traditions of the country. So that in matters of love one should be guided by the personal tastes of the woman and please her desires, even if her tastes may be different from most of the other women in her province."

On the other hand, some primitive cultures have cruelly stifled women's sexual participation and even denied them the right to show emotions during the sex act. Interestingly enough, the more enlightened and culturally developed a society was, the more active a sexual role was played by the women in it. However the pressures of society cannot be overstated as anthropologists like Margaret Mead have proved again and again. In her book The *Coming of Age in Samoa,* Ms. Mead showed that puberty and sexual awakening in a primitive, no-taboo society can be a simple and easy thing and not the painful, psychologically scarring experience it is in our society. We simply don't develop our individual patterns of sexual behavior as a result of biological heredity alone. Our sexual responses are not pure instinct as determined by the function of genes and chromosomes. From our first years, we are taught about sex, directly or indirectly, so that after our parents, grandparents, and Aunt Fanny have laid their personal sexual hang-ups on us, we get to school and there society via peer pressure finishes the job.

With the sexual revolution (and let's keep in mind how recent that is) and the new sexual permissiveness that followed, hundreds, thousands of books and manuals have appeared on the subject of sex and satisfaction. Most of them have concerned themselves with techniques, tricks, and mechanical approaches to lovemaking, what I call the erector-set mentality. Recently there has been a spate of books on women's sexuality with more information on what we think we're feeling as opposed to what we are *really* feeling. Except for a few good exceptions, all of these books have been written by men in singles or teams. Masters and Johnson is a husband and wife team whose contribution to sexology is monumental and in a class by itself, although it's not very easy reading. The other "love books" where men explain our bodies, reactions, and needs to us, range from hilariously ridiculous to downright outrageous. The end result is a lot of confusion. I'll go into this in detail in Chapter Six. The most unfortunate result of this great wealth of contradictory theories, rules, psychological, physiological fact and fiction, is what I call rabbit fever—meaning if we're not continually banging away like bunnies, having and giving paroxysms of pleasure each time, there is something wrong with us. There is a whole new industry now of books by psychologists telling how much psychic damage is done us by this onslaught of complex and mechanical approaches to sex, producing performance pressure and anxiety. Let's forget the sex secrets and, keeping in mind what we know about our bodies, see if the uncontrived Slow & Easy approach doesn't take some of the pressure off, while bringing more of the pleasure on!

Getting in the mood for sex is a different thing for different women and for the same woman on different occasions. A possible explanation of this is that in human beings, the most recently developed areas of the brain appear to be those that control sexual behavior. These are the areas most dependent on learning and intelligence capacity. Because our personalities and our experience is so varied, there is no single, failsafe technique for preparation. In the old days of sexual repression when we dared not "go all the way" outside of marriage, the charming institution of petting still existed. Petting had a lot going for it except its frustrating no-action wrap-up, of course. But when we still took time and pleasure in petting we discovered all the lovely erogenous (pleasure) zones which were our bodies' secrets, like the instep of the foot, the nape of the neck, the palm of the hand.

All this went by the wayside with the advent of the Pill and permissiveness. Now we get right down to business with no fooling around. We women have lost on that one because like they say in the slogan "getting there is half the fun." Getting to know the areas of the body which really turn you on subtly (other than the obvious clitoris) is very important to creating the titillation and anticipation we need. Once you find them, let your guy in on their whereabouts and see that he pays proper attention to them before proceeding any further!

What most couples complain about to marriage counselors is the dullness of their sex life, the pitfall of familiarity: "We've gotten into a rut." "There's no excitement anymore." The reason for this seems to be that couples tend to create patterns in the way they do things and lovemaking is included; the same time of night, sometimes the same night a week, the same bed (try the living room sofa for a change), the same lights on, or worse, no lights. You get the picture. Once this pattern is established it's hard to break out of because a vague feeling of foolishness takes over when something out of character is tried, as though someone was changing the lines of the play. This rut does not suit the ever-shifting whims and fancies of the imagination and once the imagination is left out of lovemaking, boredom is not far behind. Change things around; the time of day, the room, the lights, music, candles, why not? Go off to a hotel when your budget can afford it. It's the same price as a meal out and it could really get some excitement back into things.

Make a game out of it. If your man's usual first-gesture is caressing your vulva and clitoris, make them out of bounds until he's found enough other places to caress to get you in the mood. And don't forget to caress him back because giving pleasure is a turn-on too. See how many new ways you can figure out to spark his imagination. By the way it's not true that touching and petting will bring a man to quicker orgasm. It has been observed that a man is more likely to lose control and come too quickly if he has gone uncaressed during the preparatory arousal of the woman. So you can go to it.

As to actual lovemaking techniques themselves, we know that the deep-touch nerves in the PC muscle respond only to firm touch. This means they do not receive stimulation impulses well unless they offer resistance to the stimulus. Tension, created by contraction and relaxation, will provide this, but *only* if the muscle itself is in good enough tone to be able to produce the tension.

We now know more about the mechanism of orgasm and although all the mysteries are not yet solved, we know a lot more about how to promote that mechanism. Let's look at the way nerves are stimulated during intercourse. Stimulation is transferred via a kind of cluster of nerve cells called proprioceptors which respond to pressing and stretching. To understand this, try the following experiment: straighten one of your fingers, tensing it. Then curl it up as tightly as you can, straighten and curl it a few more times, deliberately and with effort. You will feel very clearly the impressions of the changing positions along with the stretch and contraction of the muscles. The nerve endings which provide those sensations are similar to the ones in the musculature surrounding the vagina. Now make the same finger motions as rapidly as you can and you will feel the sensations become vaguer and more blurred.

This suggests the one biggest error concerning female stimulation in intercourse—the idea that vigorous friction produces vigorous stimulation. The truth is that *slow movement is felt more clearly.* Vigorous friction as soon as the male organ enters or before the right tension is built up, is almost a sure guarantee that sensation will be blurred and that sexual tension will decline. Now go back and read this paragraph again because it will simply revolutionize your sex life!

Well, here again we blast one of the most pernicious myths to be created by porno books, magazines, and movies—fast, furious pumping will produce the most devastating orgasms. Actually when the motion is fast and forceful, the penis goes up toward the depths of the vagina which is the least sensitive area, and as the penis's deep, violent thrusts tend to knock the cervix of the uterus around, they could cause discomfort that could in turn distract from concentration of tension. Therefore while vigorous thrusts are likely to lessen a woman's sensation, they *heighten* the man's and lead the way to premature ejaculation. Now who wants that?

Counselors at the American Institute of Family Relations have developed a plan for learning good technique which seems most helpful to both partners. Once the woman has learned the PC contraction exercises, the couple is advised to begin intercourse with a slow, gentle entrance, followed by no motion at all for a while. Instead, the woman uses conscious contraction of the PC muscle. This way she feels better the kind of sensation she can get from the vagina and this helps her to focus her concentration and build tension.

At the same time, this little exercise is very pleasurable for her partner but one that does not hurl him toward speedy climax. It is possible to come to orgasm through this technique alone but thrusting seems almost a reflex action for both partners as climax nears.

Following this quiet period of contractions, the partners may start a kind of mutual, gentle motion aimed at applying pressure to the vaginal walls, thus stimulating the nerves outside the walls. It gives the woman a chance to feel her way to her own pleasure by adjusting her movements, and it teaches her partner the kind of leeway she must have to move freely. By experimenting with these gentle motions the woman gets the feel of how to dose the motions of the penis in a way that sustains or increases the sexual tension she needs to get to orgasm. During this motion a woman should be using her voluntary muscle contractions to help this along and encourage these muscles to start contracting as a reflex action. This conscious technique, the same one you use on the toilet seat while urinating, is very important. It establishes a pattern and sets off the involuntary muscle reaction which is absolutely essential to full vaginal orgasm.

Tightening the vagina around the penis deliberately *is not like cheating*; it increases tension by narrowing the walls and enabling the penis to caress all those sensitive nerve endings effectively. Nature helps this process since the walls of the vagina are ridged and not smooth. When they are thick during excitement they get narrower automatically. With our conscious efforts to narrow further, we are doing our part to help set off the trigger mechanism to orgasm. The slow, deliberate thrusts may become more vigorous toward climax and there's nothing wrong with this *provided* the orgasmic platform necessary to full satisfaction has been reached beforehand.

It may occur to you at this point that "It all sounds like work" and in a sense, it is, but the rewards are well worth the trouble. The cold hard facts are that good lovers are made and not born and the female lover, if she wants total satisfaction culminating in full vaginal orgasm, is going to have to *teach* her body to do it. It is an ability that has to be learned. Nature made things difficult for us women in that males automatically reach orgasm at the culmination of lovemaking because that is the only way their sperm can be released into the vagina. Not all orgasms in men are of equal quality and intensity but even a not-so-great come gives them release from tension and is sexually relaxing.

With us gals . . . well, I'm sure many of you know how easy it is to get pregnant not only without orgasm but without any real pleasure at all. This is nature's trap, her way of catching us in her reproduction net. With female animals it's different in that they are not interested in sex at all except when they are in heat, meaning when they can get impregnated. The rest of the time they won't let a male animal near them and are ready to fight furiously to keep him off. We can outsmart nature now with birth control methods but there's no point in outsmarting ourselves right out of orgasm by being too lazy to teach our bodies to have them. *For most women, no amount of skill or technique on the part of the man will be enough.* A woman must not merely surrender to her lover and wait for him to make things happen. She must actively seek her own body's needs. Dr. Mary Calderone, Director of SEICUS, says it this way in *Release from Sexual Tensions*:

> **You, yourself, must reawaken your body, rediscover and re-educate it . . . find out for yourself how it feels to touch yourself in certain places. Find out which places arouse the most pleasure in you when touched. Communicate these discoveries to your husband.**

Actually if we keep in mind where the sensitive areas are in the vagina and that gentle, long strokes are best suited to their stimulation, it is clear that the *slower, more deliberate manner* is less fatiguing. If you're going to pant, it ought to be from passion and not from being worn out with a lot of useless gymnastics. Earlier I explained how the outer portions of the vulva, particularly the labia minora, became thick and distended. This part of the now-lengthened vagina, roughly the first three inches, is the most sensitive area. The man should concentrate on this area with the glans, or head of the penis, since that is his thickest part. Stimulation is just as keen when he withdraws with his glans as when he penetrates. I do not mean total withdrawal to completely outside the vagina but almost. This deliberate, regular stroking does the absolute maximum in building tension for the woman if she is contracting her PC simultaneously. This brings us to the question of the best position which is most suited to no-rush, no-sweat lovemaking.

There is certainly no harm in experimenting with different positions. But if the object is to procure satisfaction where there has been none or little, exaggerated postures are likely to fail. They often introduce a mechanistic aspect to things which is more distracting than anything else. These are for when you can have orgasms at will. Even using a pillow is not a good idea. Keep things simple.

We know that traction applied to the inner lips is transferred to the clitoris. We also know that the movement of the mons, the fatty tissue overlying the vulva on which the pubic hair grows, is also transmitted to the clitoris. In fact, the clitoris is attached to the mons. Indirect stimulation of the clitoris during no-rush lovemaking is very desirable, and in fact direct stimulation should be avoided while learning the PC techniques. The reason for this is that if that is the way you've been coming the chances are it has become a crutch and your vaginal techniques have been neglected.

The face-to-face position, the good old missionary position (I call it the mama-papa way), has a lot going for it. Among other things, in this position the man's pubic bone is pressed against the woman's and the rhythmic movement is felt by the clitoris. The woman can heighten this effect by pressing toward her partner. One of the biggest psychological assets of face-to-face is precisely the face. You can see each other's faces. The amount of pleasure and stimulation in that facet alone cannot be measured. Since the woman should be free to move, some form of face-to-face position is suggested. I personally prefer lying on my side, the left for some reason. I find that in this way I am free to move, free to caress, and even change positions with my legs in all sorts of interesting ways, *without* losing a beat.

I want to close this chapter with two important points concerning performance anxiety and how it gets in the way of the Slow & Easy technique. One has to do with the size of the man's "tool." In this area, we have again fallen victim to myths concerning size-equals-sexual-ability. If we women have gotten hung up on small breasts when big ones were in, can you imagine what a man with a small penis must feel. Every sexual reference in those myth-creating pornos I love to knock, talks about the colossal dong of the male sex object. Well it's all so much bull; a big organ can get in the way in every sense of the word. A woman has to learn to dodge its thrusts to avoid being caused real pain. It can cause lubrication problems and cervix problems. Besides, with what we know now about where the vagina is most sensitive, we know that a three-inch tool can do the job. In fact experiments have proved just that.

So if your guy is small, tell him it's actually an advantage in that he can never hurt you deep inside. And don't think you have to keep riding him with the woman-on-top position to compensate for his size. That's not the best position for a woman who wants to learn orgasm. A side-by-side facing position will procure deepest penetration and all the other benefits talked about. Helping your guy overcome an utterly unjustified complex will make him a much better lover.

The other big cause of performance anxiety is the concentration on nothing but the climax. Remember always that lovemaking involves *love*, an expression of affection. You should think about technique obviously, but not exclusively because what happens in the woman is the fear, "will I fail again?" When you've got that to deal with it can become a monstrous obstacle. While doing your contractions (and mind you, you'll only have to do them consciously until your body has learned to do it on its own, as a sort of reflex action), look at his face, the pleasure you're giving him. With your fingertips, play with his lips, which become very sensitive, and then his eyelids. You don't have to *think* about contractions, you just have to do them with your vagina. Your mind is free to play erotically, and so is the rest of your body.

With men the fear is often: "Can I keep from coming long enough?" and "Will I make her come this time?" If both of you worry about these questions while lovemaking, the results are going to suffer. Anxiety is the worst enemy of sexual release in women and of control in men. Try not to pressure yourselves and concentrate on pleasuring yourselves. If you miss vaginal orgasm, you can masturbate for yourself and your lover and get some release from that. If he comes too quickly, be patient and help him to get another erection *without pressure*. Remember gratitude can go a long way toward gratification.

Dr. Albert Ellis, leading sexologist and head of the Institute for Rational Living in NYC says: "The art of love is in savoring each phase of the experience, seeking the maximum of pleasurable sensations rather than a neurotic hurrying toward release while anxiously doubting the outcome." Remember, lovemaking is a form of self-expression, a language. You reveal yourself with every move, every gesture. Try to express what you are in the most positive way you can. Then help your lover do the same.

CHAPTER SIX

ANY WOMAN CAN—BUT NOT WITH DR. REUBEN

SCENE: They were on position number ten. This one was listed under the chapter Sauces and Pickles in the newest sex how-to book Sam had brought home. Liza had promised she would go through them all until they had acquired what was guaranteed on the jacket "new dimensions in your sex life." It's not that their old sex life was one-dimensional, but after seven years of marriage, things do tend to become somewhat routine. A bit of re-education seemed in order.

Secretly, both had their own little torments as they read up on where the new sexuality was at. Liza was worried that she wasn't imaginative enough to keep Sam's interest. And Sam read repeatedly that women could and should have more, much more, than one orgasm per lovemaking session. So they were trying very hard to live up to the "new standards" and turn into dynamite partners for each other. It wasn't always easy, or fun!

Liza was balanced, not too well, on one leg and had the other wrapped around Sam's waist. Sam was attempting to penetrate from his standing position but kept losing his grip on Liza's hips. They figured out it might be easier if Sam braced himself by standing against the wall, so they unraveled themselves, moved back a few feet to the wall, and tried it again. By the time they had it back together, Sam had lost his erection and Liza had a cramp in her leg. He was muttering cursewords under his breath and she was thinking how foolish she felt. "For God's sake, let's just go to bed," she moaned. "I can't get with this stuff. I must be getting old," Sam thought.

It was weeks before Liza and Sam dropped the search for "new sexual horizons" involving complicated gymnastics, endless sex aids, and countless theories about what "should" and "shouldn't" be happening in the sack. Then it took them months before they completely lost the anxieties the sex guides had caused them and were able to find pleasure in each other again.

The subject of sex guides reminds me of what the late Jacqueline Susann said about Philip Roth after reading *Portnoy's Complaint*. Her succinct comment was, "I wouldn't like to shake hands with him."

After cutting my way through the jungle of sex manuals written by men during the last several years, my feeling is this: While I wouldn't mind shaking hands with them, I would definitely not like to *sleep* with any of them! It isn't their technical information that offends me as much as their approach to women and our bodies.

The tone of voice is prissy and purse-mouthed. They deal with such "naughty" things as female masturbation and oral sex like bad little boys in the playground.

When Dr. David Reuben gives his jocular approval of cunnilingus, I can feel his shudder of distaste. He makes his living off female genitalia, but his squeamishness is evident.

He talks about nymphomania, for instance, as an "ironical disease." Since when is nymphomania a disease at all? Nymphomania is not a medical or even an emotional disease. It is a mythical disease, created by men who think that women who like and enjoy sexual pleasure are sick. The two basic symptoms of nymphomania are these:

The woman who wants to make love when her mate doesn't is a nymphomaniac.

The woman who has more than one sex partner is a nymphomaniac.

Dr. Reuben is a medical doctor. For him to define nymphomania as a disease reveals a puritanical attitude toward women's sex drives. Clearly, he disapproves of women who sleep around. "Nymphos," he says, "can have an orgasm as long as there is little chance of repeating it." How he knows this is not explained.

Having conceded that a nympho *can* have an orgasm, he contradicts himself by saying, "Orgasm among nymphomaniacs is as rare as orgasm among prostitutes but both groups know how to protect an image.

In a section of his book he *should* have called "Fear of Fucking," Dr. Reuben expresses his unconscious fear of the vagina with a long anecdote about some mythical man named Gene whose penis got "clamped" in a frigid woman's vagina. "Her whole business clamped right down on me. I felt like I was caught in a bear trap!"

After a lurid description of being locked together, screams, terror, cops breaking down doors—and ultimate release, the doctor concedes that most cases of vaginissmus are not as "dramatic" as the one Gene experienced.

What angers me most about Dr. Reuben and his ilk is

that they say one thing and mean another, the most fundamental kind of dishonesty. Dr. Reuben says he is bringing truth and sexual liberation to women. What he is really doing is creating fear, distaste, and more sexual uncertainty than ever.

His contempt for the intelligence of women is evident in much of his book. Regarding vaginal foams, he questions "the ability of the user to understand instructions clearly" and cites the woman who complained, "I'd rather get pregnant than have to eat that little tube of foam every night—it tastes so awfully bitter!"

He does not explain how a woman who takes vaginal foam orally ever got pregnant in the first place. Adding insult to insult, his prize contribution to the subject of contraception is quite literally the vaginal burp. Coca-Cola, he says, is the best vaginal douche. In *Everything You Always Wanted to Know About Sex*, he explains that Coke contains carbonic acid, which kills sperm, and sugar, which explodes sperm cells. He goes on to explain that carbonation penetrates every tiny crevice of the vaginal lining and points out, cutely that it comes in a handy, disposable applicator.

Ever the romantic, Reuben recommends you don't get out of bed but merely insert the neck of the glass bottle into your vagina and slip a bowl under your hips to "catch the overflow"!

Should you be rash enough to take this advice, you have only to read Dr. R's very next paragraph in which he contradicts himself again! Douches, he says, including America's favorite soft drink, are *not* effective. With more cuteness, he explains that by the time the douche is started, "100,000 or so microscopic wigglers" are inside the uterus where no douche can reach them.

In a recent private interview, Dr. Reuben said:

"If a man cheats on his wife, it is *always* the responsibility of the wife. She is *always* doing something to bring it on, maybe not in an obvious way. So much of adultery is not sexual gratification, but using the sexual organs as a weapon."

He maintains that a woman can keep her husband from straying by keeping him at zero tension, meaning taking care of it every time it comes up! He believes the American wife is spoiled, used to taking and not giving. In other words, if women always said, "Fine! O.K.! Sure! Let's go!", she would keep her man from straying.

This is not only insulting to women but to men. It suggests that most men are horny little boys who punish their selfish, stingy wives by using their tools on other women. All the wives have to do is take away the weapon and so much for infidelity. And suggesting that wives "do it" whether they feel like it or not, whether they feel anything or not, is reducing wives to manipulating, unfeeling creatures whose main concern is keeping their husbands at any cost.

Dr. Reuben, by the way, when questioned about his own sex life, blushes modestly while saying, "Hey, what do you want to do, get me into trouble with my wife?" Now what do you think he means by that? I think Mrs. Reuben better look to her onions fast, or should I say bananas?

In specifically discussing female orgasm, Dr. R gets the cutes again. Orgasmic Impairment (O-I) results from "serious emotional deprivation during childhood and after." There's a daring statement to make. Name me one person, male or female, who has not suffered emotional deprivation during childhood or after. As if revealing the Truth of the Ages, he states O-I can be caused by (1) ignorance, (2) physiological problems, (3) fear of failure (which causes impotence in men).

He says further, "A woman frequently becomes nonorgasmic because she believes, contradictorily, that she needs sex and that she absolutely should not have it before marriage." I really do believe it's a little late in the century to "discover" the power of guilt. Certainly some women may still feel guilt about premarital sex, but surely it can't be pointed to as a major factor in keeping today's much more sophisticated women from orgasm.

There's more. "At one time in her life virtually every woman had strong sexual impulses with almost certain orgasmic capacity. Then something happened. Either mother came down hard on the entire idea of sex or a rejecting man squashed the budding orgasmic potential." There it is, something happened and it was a put-down from either mother or a man. And what if nothing happened but literally and out of sheer not knowing how to make anything happen? How many happy orgasmic women had either mothers who were down on sex or early male partners who were rejecters, or both? It takes more than that to keep a good woman down forever, dear doctor.

By the way, have you heard of Dr. R's failsafe way of knowing whether a woman has had an orgasm or not? This information is directed to the savvy guys who don't want to be taken in by women's manipulation of their egos. He says "They (women) are always willing to acknowledge an orgasm, even if they haven't had one. It doesn't cost them anything and goes a long way toward inflating the male ego." For the man who's ready to sacrifice his ego for the truth, here is the sign "they all exhibit."

"Erection of the nipples always follows orgasm in the female. In spite of heaving hips, lunging pelvis, passionate groans—no nipple erection, no orgasm. It is an accurate mammary lie detector—for those who insist on the truth." The implication here is: for he who is man enough to face the truth. This bit of scientific information is Dr. R's answer to the Peter Meter.

However the chances are that almost every woman, even those faking, could pass the Teat Test, since one of the first things that takes place in lovemaking is breast petting. This alone would produce erect nipples. A women well into a heated embrace, active enough to produce orgasm, would be excited enough already to have erect nipples. If there's a breeze, or the covers brush against her breasts, she could have erect nipples. And what about a female like me whose nipples are erect from beginning to end of sexual play? I'm probably overcompensating for the rejecting males of my early sexual bouts.

For all us masturbators and those of us playing with the idea of masturbation, look out. First Reuben maintains that children learn to masturbate from their mothers. "Discovery (or revelation by mother) of pleasant sexual feelings"—Reuben maintains that this is usually accomplished through excessive washing or handling of a child's genitals—"and the start of masturbation—prohibition (usually by mother)—guilt—continued masturbation with added guilt." I've heard of mother-hating, but this is ridiculous!

Dr. R writes that practically all girls who excite their clitoris also masturbate vaginally. Who says? Yet he does have a good word for masturbation when he maintains that vaginal itches can be cured with this technique and failing that, intercourse. So much for vaginal infections.

And in case you've never worried about oral sex being a form of perversion, Dr. R is right there to remind you of that possibility. But not to worry because he reassures you as fast as he can: "Heterosexuals needn't feel perverted when they do these things. If oral sex is a prelude to intercourse, it's hard to find anything harmful or wrong about it." But I get the distinct impression that Dr. R thinks it's dirty and those of us who prefer to get off this way, without the old in-and-out, have PSYCHOLOGICAL PROBLEMS, that's what.

Reuben establishes superhuman standards for sexual adequacy and if you fall short, you're dead. For men with early ejaculation problems, he maintains: "To a *normal* woman, it is the ultimate frustration. It stamps a man as an undesirable sexual partner—no *normal* woman is going to wait around for an encore." I know lots of women who are willing to give a guy a second, third, and even fourth chance at encore. Are they all abnormal? Besides not all women are as hung up as Reuben is about copulation. Some prefer other, subtler forms of excitement. And most are willing to make do with them until their partners have gotten over their stage fright (among other reasons for temporary impotence) and learned to hang on longer.

Why should a man who has the classical problem (usually temporary) of being trigger happy, be made to feel like a substandard swine by a sex expert? There are multiple ways he, with his partner's help, can overcome the problem. In the meantime, he can be a perfectly satisfying bedmate.

On wrapping up Reuben's lexicon of what's normal and abnormal in sex, let me cite three last gems concerning female orgasm, male potency, and lovemaking in general, which illustrate the worst of his superdramatic statements most likely to frighten unwary readers into frigidity.

FEMALE ORGASM—"The only thing that stands between any woman and an unlimited number of orgasmic experiences is about two pounds of tissue—the brain." It stands to reason that even a highly orgasmic woman, working with a vibrator or a stable of studs, is going to reach some limit some time. If satisfaction after a few orgasms doesn't slow down the pace, sheer exhaustion will. But for the woman who has not had orgasm and is looking to Reuben for help, this kind of pronouncement is going to be read as proof positive that she's a freak who can't think or react straight.

MALE POTENCY—Reuben mentions a condition he calls "copulatory impotence"—where erection is normal, penetration occurs, pelvic thrusting starts, and then all of a sudden erection disappears. He says about this, "The poor victim has two choices: he can retreat in humiliation by taking his penis out or wait a few seconds and let it come flopping out itself. Neither choice is appealing. Continuation of intercourse with a soggy organ is impossible." The heaping of scorn on a situation already described as "humiliating" is a poor show for a man who proclaims the psychological approach to sex is the only liberating way. A limp penis may not do for vaginal orgasm but it can be manipulated to work just fine for a clitoral one. And chances are that during that operation the penis will get just hard enough for penetration and then proceed to the desired turgidity on the demanding Reuben Peter Meter.

A man who turned out to be a master lover had that problem. He was very upset naturally and wanted to keep trying. I turned his attention to other variations including clitoral caressing. This hang-up occurs very often, especially in men who are very smitten or who have insecurities about being able to meet a sophisticated woman's demands. The trick the woman should know is to get his mind *off* intercourse at once and on to other forms of pleasure and other ways to orgasm. If she doggedly tries or lets him try to penetrate, things will only worsen.

Dr. Reuben's comment smacks again of his in-and-out mentality, which thinly veils his middle-class morality. Which leads me to the last point.

LOVEMAKING (general)—Reuben makes this sweeping statement: "Human destiny is constant, relentless copulation, in spite of all the barriers and obstacles. The instinctive compulsion to breed is irresistible." This description accurately applies to animals, not humans. What are our erogenous zones for? And what about all the things we love to do that *don't* lead to breeding, like petting, genital-kissing, masturbating—things that no animals do except those closest to man, the apes? Why do women want to make love outside of breeding periods? Why do the most sophisticated lovers take hours with pleasures that are merely preparation by R's standards and much less time with the breeding act itself, copulation?

Almost all biological and social scientists now agree that humans do not have an "instinctive compulsion to breed," but are strongly impelled to masturbate, pet, *and* fuck—only the latter results in breeding. There are millions of carefree copulating lovers, like myself, who never had a breeding thought once in their lives. Reuben would have us all believe we are out of the "normal" mainstream.

By propagating the myths about super cunts having unlimited orgasms, and super studs capable of whacking away non-stop with cast-iron cocks, by imposing more guilt on us couched in psychoanalytic terms, such as the idea that the desired end of lovemaking should be to reproduce, by encouraging the war between the sexes by suggesting that if our partners don't live up to super standards, we are being shortchanged and put down—Reuben creates the most damaging kind of performance anxieties imaginable.

The Sensuous Woman is a book, written by a woman, that does not make the same number of outrageous rules about normal and abnormal. However it still does a lot to establish Do's and Don'ts that can paralyze. The author is known to be an outspoken lady named Terry

Garrity although the signature is "J." Her stated purpose is to help women detect sensuality signals in potential partners and avoid the dud lover whenever possible. While this is a noble aim to be sure, signals can be misread even by experts. I will take up some main points as illustrations:

THE ART OF KISSING—Ms. G places great importance on a man's ability to kiss well and considers this a sure-fire indication of his know-how in the sack. Well, it could be otherwise. Kissing like a lot of other techniques has to be learned; women are probably conditioned through earlier practice to develop it as an art than men are. I've met many a man who couldn't kiss worth a damn but was a maestro on the mattress. Little girls kiss more than little boys, each other, parents, other grownups. Kissing for boys is supposed to be sissy-like and the minute peer pressure starts operating, little boys prefer demonstrations of affection to be limited to hand-shaking or some other such "manly" gesture. When they do start kissing girls, they've usually got petting on their minds and kissing is merely a means to an end. Once they've reached their "ends" they've got other things to concentrate on. So one day a woman, probably a mistress, must "teach" a young or not so young man the art of kissing.

SIGNS OF SICKIES AND PERVERTS—Ms. G feels that it's OK for a man to want to lick honey from your pussy but if he wants to resort to whips and chains or worse, wants to have you urinate on him, he's a sickie and should go out and find his like or, better yet, get professional help. Here we are again on what is normal and what isn't. Every now and then a little whipping and chaining can be fun. Who's to say that a bit of urinating goes over the line? If someone is obsessive about wanting or needing one particular trick constantly in order to get off, it is an indication that they are hung up. But that trick can be as seemingly innocent as nibbling on an earlobe. It's not what a person does that suggests deviation, it's how the doing affects him that counts. Our attitudes concerning what we do are much more important than the actual act itself. Therefore a far-out request from an imaginative, empassioned lover can be a completely "normal" trick to try. Likewise a less "kinky" act, if it becomes a necessity to satisfactory sex play, could conceivably be a sign of obsession to look out for.

LOVE, THE OPEN SESAME TO SENSUALITY—"There is only one aphrodisiac in this world and that is love," says Ms. G. Love is certainly important but not an absolute necessity to satisfying sex. You can like a person just well enough and still find him a great partner in the sack. We have gotten past the time when we had to lie to ourselves about being *In Love* in order to justify making love. Still we women have a tendency to want to be more involved in order for the lovemaking to be more meaningful. It can sometimes be a mistake. If you're with someone you love and have some kind of commitment to, and with whom this is reciprocal—OK. But if you happen to be with someone who wants to stay "uninvolved," your showing a need to "love" could be a turn-off. Affection, demonstrative gestures thereof, yes indeed. Love *toujours*? I'm not so sure.

SENSUALITY ALWAYS—You can hardly meet anybody these days who's willing to admit that he or she can take or leave sex. Everybody feels he has to be sexy, sensual, a turn-on. We're conditioned to think that sexual attraction and satisfaction are the most important elements of happiness. What if sex does not hold that much importance for you or your mate? What if on your list of priorities of what makes an interesting, enriching human being, sexual prowess is only fourth or fifth? We tend to make sex the primary social asset, the main reason for getting married, staying married, or getting divorced. In other words, we overdo the sensuality-rating ritual. We could become so hell-bent on separating the sensuous man from the duds that what we look for exclusively is the ready-to-eat packaging. In the long run it may not be the best choice.

The aspect of Ms. Garrity's book which I find outright offensive is her sexism concerning women. Even Dr. Reuben is careful on this point. But Ms. Garrity sails ahead toward keeping women thinking of themselves as sexual objects with words such as these:

> **Many a woman is now putting on makeup before going to bed so that she not only looks her best while they're making love, but also will look good if he wakes up in the middle of the night and sees her sleeping away on the pillow next to him.**

Ugh! And what about smeared lipstick, eye-shadow and runny mascara? But the idea of female authority on sex pushing this phony way to be "attractive." There's more.

> **Do I ever completely remove all my makeup? Of course, but never when he's around. If he happened to come across me barefaced, I wouldn't have a nervous collapse, but I'm not looking for opportunities to display myself when I'm at my least attractive.**

What happens when her man appears with a five o'clock shadow? Does she throw up?

> **But have I talked enough of love? For it's love that makes a woman whole. To man, love and life are things apart. To a woman, love is life itself. By fully comprehending this, you will save yourself a lot of tears.**

By fully forgetting this and similar bilge, we women may save ourselves a lot of empty lives based solely on keeping ourselves attractive to men. Let's have better sex lives by all means, but not to the exclusion of all other sense of purpose and direction. We do not expect men to do this. We cannot let it be expected of us. As to what is expected of men, let's go on to our next book.

The Sensuous Man is signed "M" and appears to be the work of none other than "J's" brother, John Garrity. It is a book directed to men, obviously, and attempts to do for men what *The Sensuous Woman* theoretically does for women. There are a number of allusions to women and sexuality naturally since after all it does take two to tango. Without dwelling too much on the sexist and puritanical elements (sis's influence, no doubt) I would like to go into some salient points concerning women and a few others which are particularly performance-anxiety-making in men.

AVOIDING EARLY EJACULATION—SM maintains that none of the tricks recommended by sex specialists to solve men's greatest problem in sex is going to work, i.e., masturbating before making love, spraying the penis with a local anesthetic cream, wearing a rubber, thinking of something else. In other words if the guy doesn't have the willpower and self-control to do it without any help from anyone or anything, he's rotten to the core plus being a lousy lover. This adds so much guilt to disappointment that a poor guy could end up permanently disabled as far as hanging on in is concerned. Masters and Johnson have developed extraordinarily effective techniques to handle this thorny problem; *SM* pooh-poohs those by saying if they work, the sex will be lousy anyway. Absolutely not true, and again I have personal experience to back me up: I once had a most remarkable lover who was so turned on when we got together that he could never last more than five minutes. We didn't have to resort to condoms or to anesthetising creams such as Nupercainal (which a guy puts on and washes off *before* screwing, incidentally). Not that there's anything wrong with these, it's just that the Masters and Johnson trick worked all by itself. I would masturbate him until he got near ejaculation then I would circle the glans with my forefinger *gently* until the desire subsided. Then we'd do it again. This way he learned to feel the rhythm of his sexual peaking *in my presence, with me helping him*, and could concentrate on his control. After a few sessions of this he could go on and on until I cried Uncle.

RETARDED ORGASM—This is a tricky problem to lick in men. *SM* writes this off as strictly psychological and in need of immediate help before the joy of intercourse wanes with the "growing concern" of the female. There's a comment calculated to keep the boys up at night. Though there are often psycholgical reasons for this problem there are also tricks that very often help overcome it. Furthermore the problem may be physiological and require the help of medical sex specialists of which there are many. There are books available on this subject which are excellent. Just don't be goaded into "awfulizing" about it. You can probably conquer it.

NYMPHOMANIACS—Mr. Garrity, like Dr. Reuben, writes off women concerned with a lot of sex a lot of the time as nymphomaniacs too easily. There are a lot fewer nymphomaniacs around than we imagine and puritanical judgments like Garrity's don't help people get over their prejudices. What would normally be considered as rather a admirably robust sexuality in a man is easily dubbed nymphomania in a woman. Nymphomania is a rather rare psychological more than physiological disturbance and must be treated as such. However to say as he does that nymphomaniacs are just on ego trips and are always takers, not givers, is not only judgmental but inaccurate. Nymphos can be terrific in bed and many a young man has had a lot to thank them for. A nymphomanic woman may be using sex to look for something no man can give her, but while she's looking she's picking up a lot of experience. Just because she's not concerned with fidelity is no reason to put her down as being of no interest. And speaking of fidelity . . .

MARRIED WOMEN—Here Mr. Garrity joins his sister in moralizing. Get this: "I personally don't believe that a single man should inject himself into a married woman's life, because he has little control over the effect his presence may exert on her husband and her children—not to mention the marriage itself. I have little respect for the bachelor who breaks up marriage after marriage by seducing women who are only looking for a little sympathy and excitement." Ugh!

The number of false assumptions in this statement and the underlying double standard and sexism boggles the mind. First what if the single man was *invited* into the life of the married woman instead of *injecting* himself on his own? What if she loves her husband but the sex isn't so great anymore, or never was their main thing together? What if she feels the need to express herself elsewhere because she's tired of the siamese twin act in bed and in banter? Why *assume* that this will affect her life with her spouse or children? Men so easily believe that they can control their emotions in extramarital relations; why do they assume women can't? And why should bachelors alone be called reprehensible when they seduce poor, bored wives? The biggest seducers are married men who are bored out of their skulls themselves, or who aren't getting enough at home. Remember the cliché no dummy will use anymore—"My wife doesn't understand me"? And what's wrong with a wife looking for a little sympathy and excitement? It could very likely do wonders for her marriage.

I am not saying that all married women should go after affairs, not by a long shot. I'm not even sure that "swinging" is as successful a phenomenon as it's drummed up to be. But I do say that anyone who can say to women these days that the fidelity vow is sacred, that marriage is the beginning and end of their sexual lives, anyone who can imply that straying is harmful to women while being just naturally naughty for men, is grinding the wrong ax!

There is a very serious sexologist who writes regular articles in popular sex mags designed to enlighten the sensualist with a *Reader's Digest* mentality. He also writes long, in-depth books and has a list of professional credits which establishes him as an expert on the subject of sex. His name is Dr. Robert Chartham and while he is head and shoulders above the Garritys, it's the same old pressure to perform, to be moral, to be straight.

In his book *The Sensuous Couple*, Chartham says that the sensuous couple *never*: makes love in the dark, under the blankets, or plans in advance to have sex. Furthermore the couple *always*: spends at least an hour at sex, preferably two hours, have orgasms not less than two hours after they've finished eating a meal (I thought that was for swimming), and that sex is best between 6:00 and 8:00 A.M. (*sic*). Now if these rules seem a bit on the rigid side, there are reasons for them and Dr. Chartham warns: "You may think you are getting away with it when you are young, but you are really laying up trouble for yourself later on. When you're fifty-five or sixty you wouldn't like to put your Sensuous Partner in the embarrassing situation of having a coronary while you're coupling, would you?" Now if that hasn't put the fear of God into you, nothing will.

As to women's response to a Chartham-trained lover the good doctor says: "Any Sensuous Woman can, like the male, be aroused at will if her partner is a Sensuous Man." Whose will? What if she's tired, upset, sick, what if she damn well doesn't feel like it? What kind of automatons does he think we all are?

For the flagging lover, Chartham says to the gals to find the man's erection center which is located somewhere in the small of the back. A couple of caresses and he's flying high again ready for more action. There is such a thing as an erection center in the small of men's backs. It is deep under the skin, however, and not very accessible to even a doctor's probing. So women are going to feel like fools because there they are kneading away at the small of their guys' backs until they are black and blue and never find the up button. To the guys he says, now get this, "Suck her big toe. It doesn't matter on which foot. If she squirms or groans, you can be sure that you can pull out all the stops and be thoroughly appreciated." Zounds! This one sounded too good to be true so I got my guy and said, "Now I know this is going to sound kinky, but I'd like you to do something special." I assured him that my feet were freshly bathed and kissing clean. He looked at me as though this time I had really blown my lid. Well on we, he, went and I've got to admit, it feels good. Nothing crazy mind you, no groans or moans, but yes, it did feel good. But so did the next to the big toe, and the other little ones. My feet happen to be very erogenous. But nothing special happened with the big toe. Now Chartham guarantees this big toe bit, so I guess I'm a washout as far as being a sensuous person by his book.

More absolutes: "The secret of the Sensuous Couple's lovemaking is that they each work on the other simultaneously." Oh yeah? Not me, not a lot of people I know. The sixty-nine scene is very big in pornos but not in fact. For me it ruins concentration. I'd rather go in turns depending on who's inspired or on fire.

Chartham also feels that really sensuous people, if allowed only one kind of caress to the exclusion of all others, would choose the blow job. A mutual blow job, that is. I've done a lot of inquiring on this one and not one source has ever said blow job, either mutual or in turns.

I'll bring my scoring of the sex experts to an end here with what I hope will be considered a couple of sound, simple conclusions:

1. Technique is fine, very important, but it should be a means to an end, *NOT THE END*.

2. "Fancier" lovemaking may be a kick now and then but there is nothing wrong with having a favorite tried and true position that you and your partner are happy with. That does not make you "square" because if it works for you, nobody can tell you it's wrong.

3. Before adding instruction, the main ingredients to good lovemaking are patience, compassion, and affection. Without these as a base, we run the risk of missing the "human encounter" which is the difference between lovemaking and "having sex."

CHAPTER SEVEN

THE JUICY BLUES

SCENE: Laurie and Don had been dating steadily for over a month. There was no question about it, they really thoroughly enjoyed each other. Furthermore they really turned one another on as they discovered on their most recent dates where they couldn't keep their hands off each other. In fact if they hadn't "gone all the way" before it was because they both wanted their first time together to be *perfect*. They had both been married and they knew what they felt for each other was more, a lot more than a mere infatuation. In the backs of their minds they were thinking "This could be it" so they wanted the sex to be just right.

"It took me a year of marriage to find out I didn't love my husband's body," Laurie said. "It's a mistake I don't want to make again."

And Don had told her about his marriage: "Mary just

didn't like sex. After three years of marriage and a child, she thought she was sure enough of me to finally confess it: she never liked it. Two years of therapy later she hadn't changed and we broke up."

Obviously they both had a lot riding on this affair-to-be so the setting had to be just right. Imagine a seaside cottage, French doors opening onto a starlit sandy beach, inside a small fire going and for dinner, cold lobster, white wine, and cheese by candlelight. Atmosphere notwithstanding, when they at last reached the high moment of the evening and their bodies came together on the shag rug in front of the fireplace, something awful happened: Laurie's vagina was tight and dry, so much so that it was obvious to Don that he couldn't possibly penetrate without causing her real pain. They let it go for a while.

"This sort of thing happens very often the first time around . . . par for the course," he said glibly. "I feel so foolish. It's not as though I were a virgin or something." They talked awkwardly of other things while thinking of one thing only. When they tried again, this time in a huge, comfortable bed—things were no better, perhaps a little worse: Laurie's whole vulva was dry so that Don couldn't even caress her with his hands without causing friction. "Jesus, it's the same scene all over again, I'm doomed," he thought. Laurie was despondent. "He's going to think I'm frigid." They tried to console each other by saying that not every couple can be sexually compatible but each felt a deep sense of failure.

The next day, determined to finish the weekend on an up beat, they went for a picnic in the dunes. Don was determined not to let sex stand in the way of their friendship. "I can't blame myself if the chemistry was all wrong, it's just one of those things." Off the hook as it were and almost feeling relieved about it, they felt free to hold hands, hug, caress each other without worrying about the "big moment" which was to follow. As Laurie watched a sailboat maneuver in the distance, Don reached over and kissed her cheek. It was as though an electric shock had shot through them. In seconds they were in each other's arms and shortly thereafter they were the happiest of lovers on a deserted dune.

Laurie and Don's experience is not uncommon. In fact it is a classic wedding night situation that starts many a couple off on the wrong sexual foot if they don't understand what's happening. In Don's case things worked out because when he and Laurie stopped *worrying* about whether they would work out or not, the pressure was off. But Don had the good sense not to push things. A less experienced man, an eager young husband, for example, unwilling to let his bride and his expectations down, might push ahead, disappointing himself and turning an inexperienced young woman off sex for a long time.

Lubrication, which is a kind of sweating of the vaginal walls, happens very quickly in women. As quickly as ten seconds after strong stimulation, a woman's whole vagina and vulva can be moist and ready for penetration without discomfort. The kind of stimulation that triggers this phenomenon depends on the individual woman. For some it can be the simple sight of The Man. Or it can be the sight of an anonymous man who sets off sexual associations with the way his hair falls on his forehead. A crush on a movie star has moistened many a moviehouse seat. It can happen long before kissing and petting begin.

Tumescence, or the thickening of the vulva, is not the first thing as most people think, but the second. If nature put lubrication first, it must mean that it is a very important part of the action. In fact it is the essential part, because without it, penetration is painful and the female will avoid it. Therefore trouble with lubrication can be very disturbing to a woman who is eager and ready to make love. But no matter how eager or anxious to please she is, no woman should allow intercourse if she is not moist enough. Lack of moisture means she has not been stimulated enough and the body is not tuned into love. If she goes ahead anyway, the result is likely to be the painful and humiliating "dry fuck."

Many bad jokes have been made about the *dry fuck* but when it happens to you, you know it's not funny. There are a number of reasons for this condition and I'll try to get to all of them. The first and most common is because the woman is not ready. If this happens to you, take the time and do the things that make you ready. My friend Jean has a little trick she swears by. Her guy has to travel with his job at least one week out of three and when he gets home after that long week away, he's raring to go. Jean found that it almost always took her more time than a big bear hug and long wet kiss to "get into the mood" even though the week had been a long one for her also. So when her lover called from the airport to say "light the logs and cool the wine, I'm on my way" she would masturbate herself to climax a few times. When he flew in the door she was just as ready as he was.

We don't always have the time and the opportunity to prepare Jean's way, but ninety percent of the time, not enough foreplay is the answer. Don't skimp in this area and don't let your lover's urgings sway you. Encourage him to caress you with his hands or kiss your vulva with his tongue and lips. This will usually do the trick for the gal who just hasn't been primed enough.

No matter how insistent he becomes, remember there is no need for you to feel you have to be the ever-ready Sex Goddess at all times. Don't be petulant but don't give in just the same. Get him involved in a game of caress exchanges: "First you do this to me and if you do it real good, you can ask me to do some for you." It may sound silly but under the right circumstances it's a real turn-on. If things really get rough, bring him to climax first and then start all over again. He'll be less explosive the second time around.

If anxiety is keeping you tense and dry and no amount of foreplay seems to do the job even though you really dig your guy, there are ways to get things going until nature takes its course. Saliva works wonders. It can come from your lover's kisses directly to your vulva or he can moisten his own hand with it as he caresses you. Or it can come from your own mouth on your own hand as you caress yourself. Saliva is the closest you can come to the texture of your own vaginal moisture and you should resort to it constantly.

Sometimes when you make love a second or third time around you can run out of juice . . . from both ends. Or if your guy uses a condom, saliva may not be enough to lubricate you sufficiently. You can use K-Y jelly, which is available in any pharmacy without a prescription. It is odorless and more important, harmless to your delicate tissues. It should do the lubricating you need just fine. Another source of quick and harmless lubrication is vaginal foam used for contraception or any jelly or cream used with a diaphragm.

Whatever you do, don't use petroleum jelly; it is very irritating to sensitive membranes and should never be put in the vagina, despite all the stories we were told about its usefulness in "tight situations." If your tight situation persists, you should see a gynecologist because your dryness and tightness may be caused by a vaginal infection. These can creep up on us without warning and will just hang on, causing all kinds of irritations until they are cleared up. Vaginal pain during intercourse can be the result of:

1. *Monilia or Trichonomodes*: common vaginal infections usually caught from a carrier-partner. Can be cleared up with a special douche your doctor will prescribe. By the way, a friend of mine has found a homeopathic cure for monilia. She inserts plain yogurt with her vaginal injector. She swears a few days' treatment clears it up.

2. *Allergic Reactions*: to rubber of a condom or to your vaginal jellies or creams. Change brands if you think that's the problem.

3. *Hygienic Sprays*: all those dreadful "feminine deodorants," which get past the pure food act control because they are in the cosmetic category, are *dangerous*. Do not use them under any circumstances. They can give you sores which will take months to clear up and much worse. Besides don't be brainwashed into washing away your natural odor. Just keep clean.

4. *Excessive Douching*: keeping clean means an occasional douche, such as after your period. *Not* after every lovemaking session and *not* every day. Your vagina is self-cleaning if there is no infection. When you douche do *not* use soap, vinegar, or salt. Just lukewarm water will be fine. There are natural, necessary bacteria in your vagina which protect it from many infections. Overdouching will destroy these, make you vulnerable to infection, take away your very personal odor, and take away natural lubrication. So you see, there's every reason to avoid it.

5. *Hormone Imbalance*: sometimes, after childbirth for instance, or at menopause, your hormone balance can go awry. Again, your gynecologist can help you with this, sometimes with a treatment as simple as vaginal suppositories. If you really want expert advice, see an endocrynologist.

I want to go back to the question of vaginal tastes and smells for a moment because there is much confusion on the subject. We women have been railroaded into thinking that any vaginal odor is bad and must be eliminated in order to keep us "feminine." Nothing could be further from the truth because any man who knows will tell you that a woman's vaginal odor is a very personal and exciting thing. However there are times when the odor and taste is particularly strong, and, as during the menstrual period, over-lubrication can be a problem also. There are a few tips I can give you about both.

Concerning the over-lubrication of the menstrual flow, I'm sure no one has to tell you how inconvenient that can sometimes be. Have you planned for a special weekend or vacation with your lover only to discover you've started menstruating the second you arrive? I happened upon a handy way to take care of that problem by using an old diaphragm to "catch" the menstrual flow. Even if it's one of your heavy bleeding days, if you insert your diaphragm just before lovemaking (no jelly required), it will keep the flow out of your way until you take it out afterward. Then during your days of lessening flow, you can just leave it in the whole night and no one will be the wiser and you won't be inconvenienced.

As to the smell, which can be more pungent just before your period begins and certainly during and immediately after, remember your lukewarm douche to wash away the bits of membrane that can stick to vaginal walls and cause odors. Another thing to do to keep clean is to wrap cotton around your index finger until you've made a swab out of it, slightly moisten this so it won't stick to the vaginal walls, and reach into your vagina. Once you've reached the cervix (don't be squeamish, find it!) just roll your cotton finger around it and wipe away the excess blood and membrane particles. Now you can be sure you're clean.

If you still think your odor is a bit strong I can pass on a tip my French women friends recommend as failsafe. They cut cucumbers into peeled bite-size (no pun intended) morsels and insert them in their vaginas for an hour or so before seeing their lovers. I tried this and found it to be very effective.

Cucumbers have been used since Cleopatra's day for all kinds of face and body creams. Not only do they have an astringent quality to them (this won't hurt the vagina) but their perfume blends beautifully and naturally with the musk of the skin. In the vagina, my friends contend, they actually absorb odors. There's nothing to lose, and I assure you, if nothing else, it's very refreshing.

Sometimes having eaten a certain food will give your vaginal sweat a strong odor. Garlic is famous for this, and asparagus never misses. Unless these turn your guy on and you know that for a fact, go for the cucumber following a douche. Otherwise dodge the garlic at least, if possible.

With the number of hints and tricks I've suggested in this chapter, ordinary, run-of-the-mill lack of lubrication in the vagina should no longer be a problem for you. Do keep your K-Y jelly close at hand (closer than the bathroom; it should be in the drawer of your night table), so that you don't have to break a mood by getting up and going out of the bedroom. And don't be squeamish about saliva because it is the absolute best lubricant there is. After all nobody worries about saliva when passionate open-mouthed kisses are being exchanged, right?

The other advice I'd like to give in closing this chapter is for heaven's sake don't be apologetic about your vaginal taste and odor. It is important to keep clean of course but you shouldn't taste or smell of soap. Your "intimate" taste and perfume is as personal as your handwriting. Learn to show it off, to love it. Your lover will do the same.

CHAPTER EIGHT

MASTURBATION: END YOUR FEAR OF FLYING SOLO

SCENE: Sandra's honeymoon had been a disaster. She and Jack made jokes about how they would recount it to their grandchildren and laugh out loud. "The kind of honeymoon bad jokes are full of," said Jack. But by the time they were on their trip back home, their laughter had become very brittle. Sandra was just not responding sexually and that was that. Before their wedding they had petted, fondled, and on a few occasions, hurried, guilty ones, they had "made it." Sandra had seemed to enjoy all that. Had the thrill gone just because they had become legitimate?

The irritability grew between them. Jack resented being rejected and Sandra resented Jack's pushing too hard, "not giving me enough time." A month after their marriage Jack was ready to give up and Sandra was ready to see a shrink. Then one night Jack got a brilliant idea. As they undressed for bed he couldn't help feel the tension grow as Sandra began to steel herself against his assault. Instead of approaching her he said, "Look babe, let's lay off screwing for a while, it's not all it's cracked up to be anyway." As Sandra's eyes widened, he began to caress himself. Then he turned off the lights and in the dark he encouraged her to do the same. Sandra confessed she didn't know how. She also confessed she never enjoyed intercourse even before their wedding, she had been faking. Jack asked her to try caressing herself, for him, for his pleasure and assured her he would not try to make love to her. Out of relief and gratitude she tentatively began to explore her vulva with her fingers and once she started relaxing, she started feeling.

Within a few days she was looking forward to this nightly exploration of her own body. Jack would encourage her with gentle, unpressured words: "Just take it easy and see where it feels best. Nothing to worry about, nothing to feel funny about. It's your body, you've got a right to be nice to it." Sandra had never masturbated as a child, she had always been made to think it was a filthy thing to do. So she had a long way to come from that childhood shrinking away from touching herself to actually giving herself pleasure. The sensation in her genitals was a totally new experience and doing it with and for Jack made it very exciting. Within a week she was no longer doing it for Jack but for herself and then one night it happened, she had an orgasm, her first in her whole life. She and Jack were able to become lovers very soon afterward.

Not all husbands are as insightful or as patient as Jack, unfortunately. And not all women have husbands to lead the way to auto-sexual responsiveness. But that's okay, because you don't need a husband or anybody else for that matter. All you need is curiosity, good will, and a few helpful tips. The rest is up to you if you are determined to reach your full sexual potential.

The reasons why a woman is non-orgasmic are many but the least common one is the one that is most frequently referred to—frigidity. Very few women are frigid since it is a very serious disturbance requiring medical and/or psychiatric attention. What is meant, when the term frigid is bandied about, is a nonresponsive woman. A woman may not be able to outgrow her childhood fear or guilt about sex. She may have an excessive fear of pregnancy which even effective birth control cannot erase. She may have been caught masturbating as a little girl and so severely chastized and made to feel ashamed that she can no longer think of her genitals without those feelings returning. She may have been made to feel so suspicious of men that even love and the security of marriage cannot change her.

For whatever reasons girl children are made to fear and worry about sex more than boy children, one thing is always assumed: "When the right time comes (meaning marriage usually) everything will come naturally." This is simply not always the case. Some women move easily away from the nonsense about sex that is laid on them, to pleasure and enjoyment. Others get stuck and even though in their heads they know sex is perfectly natural, for them it is not naturally perfect.

In fact "doing what comes naturally" is one of the flagrant misconceptions of all time. Copulation for the purpose of impregnation is purely instinctive; that is the way all four-legged animals *make out*. Lovemaking, physical satisfaction and relief, emotional feelings of accomplishment and well-being, *must be learned*. This is something I cannot stress often enough. We women have been taught to be passive, to wait to be courted, asked in marriage, provided with love and sex which will bring us satisfaction. All we have to do is lie there and wait and it will all happen. Wrong! Nothing will happen (except we can get pregnant) unless we learn how to make it happen, and then teach our partners what we know.

Each of us is different physiologically and psychologically. We need to know certain ground rules and a quantity of information. With that we get to know something about ourselves. *Then* we have to transmit that knowledge to our lovers because: (1) They are not mind-readers, they have to be shown what we need and want just as they have to learn whether we prefer tea or coffee in the morning. (2) They may not know enough of the bare essentials to be able to do anything for us. The burden of learning is on us because a man has an orgasm automatically (it can take as little as a few seconds) and a woman does not.

Self-stimulation is something women tend to shy away from, even though it is the most obvious way to increase sexual responsiveness in general. Whatever your reasons are for not having experimented with bringing yourself to orgasm, decide that it is a duty you have to yourself. Not only will it help you to release sexual tensions if you live alone but even if you live with someone else, it can heighten your pleasure plateau immensely. Not experiencing good sex is harder on a woman today than it was in the past because of more and more pressure on us to be liberated. It is more difficult to say no since everybody is doing it and everybody is supposed to be enjoying it.

Set aside a time during your day to devote wholly to your self-pleasuring. Make your bedroom up as if for a lover, turn on the lights and the music that will create the right mood for you. Have some oil or some other kind of lubricant handy, other than saliva of course because you may run out of that. Baby oil, massage or coconut oil, even a vegetable oil will do for our purposes. But not Vaseline since it is not water soluble and can cause irritation. Once you're set in a comfortable position and with your lubricant at hand, you can begin to explore your clitoral area.

Touch the whole area lightly with the sensitive tips of your fingers. Try not to think too much what you're doing. Try instead to just *feel*, meaning try to tune into the difference in sensation that different areas of your vulva produce. You will find some spots more sensitive than others. In fact you will find some spots actually become irritated easily, so you can leave them alone. Use feather touches at first and caress the outside of your skin first and then press a bit harder as though you were reaching for muscles underneath. Don't expect astounding results the first time around but come back next day, same time, same environment and do some more. If you have some negative reactions to this session, guilt, fear, disappointment because of overanticipation, it's okay and perfectly normal. Remember it's *your* body, the one thing that is totally yours in this life and you don't need anybody's permission or approval to do something nice for it. So, carry on.

Next time around try to prepare yourself mentally for your "work session at play" and think of erotic scenes that have turned you on. Perhaps you can go back to erotic passages in books you have read. Imagine a perfect lover in a perfect setting. Then before going directly to your clitoris, caress the other erogenous (pleasure-producing) zones you know of: your breasts and nipples, the insides of your thighs. As these begin to bring you pleasurable feelings go to your clitoris with one hand while continuing elsewhere with the other. If a little drink will get you more in the mood, let's not be stingy, go to it. But don't overdo it. You want your sensations enhanced, not dulled. It might help you to hold a mirror to your genitals as you caress. You will see the changes even as you feel the sensations. In any case this will help you to get to like yourself down there as you see what a fascinating phenomenon is going on.

Once you have managed to have a clitoral orgasm with your hand, you can try using a vibrator. There are different types of vibrators available in most drugstores or by mail order. Most women seem to prefer a small electric kind with a ball-type rubber knob which can be used directly on the clitoris. There is an intensity control so that it vibrates harder or softer depending on your desire. You'll have to experiment, possibly starting softly and around the outside of the clitoris before going directly there. Many women have been able to incorporate their vibrators into their lovemaking with their partners, before, during, and even after. I've found that men can get a real turn-on from the vibrations they can feel also. So keeping in mind that practice makes perfect, keep at it.

For heaven's sake don't be like my friend June who wouldn't use a vibrator because she's afraid to "get hooked" on it and not be able to come any other way ever. This is nonsense. All you are doing is making yourself more responsive and that means you will be more responsive with your partners, too. Just like using an exercycle in your home. The machine is working your muscles—you're not actually doing a mile of bicycling on your own. But your muscles are being developed just the same and when you do get out on a real bike, your muscles are tuned and responsive.

I must add a note at once to those women who do not like the idea of any mechanical aid to pleasuring, and do not like the idea of vibrators or dildos posing as vibrators. To these women I would strongly suggest the old standby we giggled at as youngsters—finger fucking. By using two or three fingers right inside the vagina (that first sensitive third) and contracting the PC at the same time, they should get the desired results. Actually the fingers are much more capable of feeling contractions of the vagina than any vibrator. This technique added to the clitoral caressing (at the same time if you can work that out) should do the trick.

The next step: while using your vibrator or your hand to bring yourself to clitoral orgasm, practice your PCs at the same time. This is very important if you want the whole area to come to life and not just your clitoris. It will be tricky to synchronize this at first but you can if you try and the results will be well worth the effort. I am all for making the clitoral area more aware and responsive but remember your clitoris should not become a crutch. You want the whole thing, and you can get it.

When you've got this all together, you can add another instrument to your gadget drawer and that is the vaginal vibrator. This is an instrument that looks like a banana on a pedestal. It is made of plastic, comes in different shades of pastel in addition to black and white and is battery-operated. This too can be found in most drugstores and is cutely called a "facial vibrator." Those in the know find this amusing but the fact is that it is also good for your facial muscles. But that's not our concern right this minute.

As you caress your clitoris, try moving the vaginal vibrator in a gentle in and out, just like the boys do it. While doing this, keep at your PC contractions so that all these movements become part of one basic design—to get the clitoral spasms to conduct directly to the PC and set the vaginal spasms going toward the ultimate goal—total, mind-blowing orgasm. It won't all happen at once and your first orgasm may not be mind-blowing, just so-so. That's okay because as you become more orgasmic your sensations will intensify and become more dramatic.

A friend of mine I'll call Jennie went to an orgasm

class. Yes, there are such groups and they are wonderful if everybody's head is in the right place. Jennie had a certain amount of reluctance about the group but a combination of curiosity and desire to learn new techniques egged her on. Once there, she was overcome by anxiety at the thought of exposing herself to a group of total strangers.

Jennie's group was coed and run by a well-known woman painter who is very dedicated to enhancing self-awareness and pleasure through masturbation. Jennie felt very self-conscious because the sessions were conducted in the nude and this was her first time nude in a group situation. The ground rules were no "fooling around," everybody stuck to doing his or her own thing. Vibrators were provided and oils and music and such but the most important thing provided was the feeling of togetherness with other men and women without the traditional "coupling." Jennie said she felt an incredible sense of freedom from fear and sense of discovery at the same time.

"I started first with my hand and oiled my body, caressing myself all over before settling into my cunt. There was a lovely tingling sensation all over me. I guess I felt a little heady because of the whole collective situation. I mean, the fluffy rugs and guys and women all around, about fifteen in all. People would get up and move to other areas and at first I was very aware of this. After a while it all blended into a haze and didn't matter. I began to caress myself more seriously, becoming really involved in my own sensations. But as soon as I would get near reaching an orgasm, when I came near a plateau as it's called, I moved to caressing something else, like my breast or my thigh. The idea was to prolong orgasm and keep building plateaus as long as possible, the ideal being an hour. I only made forty minutes or so but when I came it was something else. My nipples were stiffer than I'd ever seen them, and my cunt was so sensitive that toward the end the slightest touch was like electricity. I had never had an orgasm like that before."

Sounds wonderful, doesn't it? If the collective experience doesn't seem to be your bag, it doesn't matter because much the same route can be done alone. The most interesting note in Jennie's report was that she couldn't wait to get to bed with her lover after her "group session." And when she did, she told me their sex together had never been so good. The reason for that was that her sex *alone* had reached a new and *independent* high.

Woody Allen's movie "Love and Death" had a funny moment where he has just made love to a designing woman of the world. Anxious to flatter him, she says, "How did you ever become such a wonderful lover?" And he replies, "I practice a lot when I'm alone." I think he's got the right idea!

CHAPTER NINE

JOURNEY TO THE PLEASURE ZONES

SCENE: During her routine annual check-up, Lillie's doctor told her she had developed some celulite. This is a collection of fatty tissue in which the cells collect and retain water. It is caused by bad circulation and is usually found on the abdomen, rump, and thighs. A common name for flesh like this is "rotten apple ass." When she heard her doctor say this she was mortified. Furthermore he told her it would take more than dieting to get rid of her chunky deposits. It would take massages as well. So off she went to a masseur for the first time in her life.

It started with the very first massage. When the masseur, a rather plain-looking balding man with red hair, got to her calves and feet, she got wildly turned on. She had expected some reaction when he massaged the insides of her thighs and her abdomen and ass. But calves and feet! Then she discovered her shoulder blades were dynamite, and this convinced her she must be some kind of freak. As she got dressed, still heady from everything she felt, she decided she'd better talk to her doctor about it.

However that night she was seeing her lover and she got an idea. She complained of how tight her calf muscles were and how tired her feet felt after a long day. Did he mind very much massaging them for her? Not at all, said the darling man, and no sooner had he begun than stars began to twinkle under her skin, just like at the masseur's. She became delightfully passionate, being able at last to express everything she had to keep under cover when it had happened during the afternoon. Eric was surprised at the sudden change from aching muscles to lust-filled lips, but he rose to the occasion.

When she did talk to her doctor, he laughed and explained that the masseur had accidentally revealed to her a few of her undiscovered erogenous zones. These are areas which are pleasure-producing and sometimes you can find them in the strangest places. Lillie was thrilled and decided then and there to go hunting for more of these areas of her body and her lover's.

Pleasure zones are something we all know about and since there are many that men and women share in common, they usually attract the most attention. Let me name a few: ears, eyelids, lips, nape of neck, nipples, insides of thighs, buttocks. These areas more often than not get a rise out of the caressee. There are less obvious places, however, and these are the secrets of each individual body.

As far as discovering the pleasure zones is concerned, you must make the decision to set out exploring on your own. There is a lot we can find out about our bodies all by ourselves. And you don't necessarily have to have a vibrator. Just running your fingers lightly along your legs and arms and neck and body will give you some ideas about where things might happen. Using a cologne or herb-scented oil is a good idea since that will turn on your sense of smell and get you that much more in the mood.

Of course, there's nothing quite like someone else's hands to help you discover yourself. As a rule I would greatly encourage all getting-to-know-yourself explorations to be conducted *à deux.* One reason is that people just don't take enough time with each other in general. That tends to make sex functional and once that happens, it gets less interesting all around. So take your best man, turn down the lights and otherwise set a perfect scene, and find out where those zones are. Start by running the hands from the forehead softly down the cheeks and nose and eyelids (use fingertips for this) around the chin, down the sides of the neck, underneath the chin and so forth. The ears are sensitive for almost everyone, male and female, which is why whispered nothings are so exciting.

Upon doing these explorations myself I discovered a whole new thing in my lover whose body geography and reactions I thought I knew by heart. I was running fingertips down his back in flutter movements after having spent an indecent amount of time on the nape of his neck. To our mutual delight and utter surprise, his shoulder blades and area just underneath are wildly responsive. So much so in fact, that I had to measure my caresses ever so carefully so I wouldn't tickle him. It worked wonders.

There are other ways than caresses to tune your body toward love. One way is some form of exercise like yoga or modern dance. This kind of movement will get the circulation going to the very tips of the capillaries right underneath the skin. When the skin is touched the sensation is greater. Exercise also makes you generally more aware of your physical being and makes you feel better all over. There is one yoga exercise that turns me on particularly and that is the headstand, although I do a modified version of it by supporting my legs against the wall. When I hold this position for a few minutes the blood moves away from my feet, legs, and abdomen toward the upper part, chest, throat, and head. When I then move gently back to a sitting, then standing position, the blood runs back down, and as it fills the nooks and crannies of my genitals, the effect is a very subtle warming up of the whole area. Try it, I guarantee you'll like it, but do it slowly, otherwise it won't work and will only make you dizzy. A shoulder stand will also do the trick if you prefer that.

Bathing is another form of pleasuring yourself for love. A warm, not too hot, bath with an oil or herbal bath salt can do wonders to wash away fatigue and warm up every pore. Soap is not recommended because it has a tendency to dry skin rather than lubricate it. Lubrication makes it both receptive and pleasant to the touch. And sunbathing just enough to get a glow (not a burn, not even a tan) is another way to tone up and tune in to your skin and its sensitivity. The warming, soothing effect of sun especially if followed by a dip in the ocean has long been known as one of nature's divine aphrodisiacs.

The desired result in all these suggestions to how a more sensitive skin and body is developed is twofold: 1) they all help to relax you and relaxation is of prime importance where pleasure is concerned 2) they attune the mind to the body as a whole, not just its sexual parts. For sex to be good, the whole physical being should be involved and delighted.

I want to mention diet here just briefly. There are hundreds of different diets recommended for better bodies and better sex too. I won't go into any of those but I do want to talk about the effects of certain foods on body reactions. In general a more slender body is a healthier, more responsive body as well as a more attractive one. The attractive part has to do with present-day standards of beauty. At the turn of the century, plump was beautiful and skinny was turn-off time.

But esthetic standards, which are ever changing, aside, some foods can be a help to sex and others a nightmare. My own experience has shown me that eating light before lovemaking is a must. A heavy stomach keeps me down and moving around a lot can upset it. I like a little wine with a light meal but keep my drinking to a sip of cognac every now and then from a snifter I like to keep very close at hand. I don't like to drink a lot of alcohol before love because it dulls my senses rather than heightens them. I start feeling groggy and that's bad news.

When the body is digesting, blood runs to the stomach and other digestive organs so lovemaking puts things at cross purposes. Therefore eating a spicy, heavy, or otherwise hard-to-digest meal before the boudoir is not a good idea. It can bloat your lower abdomen which not only looks dumpy but can feel uncomfortable too. Oh before I forget, if you happen to have sensitive intestines like me and get constipated with any kind of excitement, for heaven's sake don't plan a big evening or weekend without rectifying the situation.

Having your bowels blocked will not only bloat you and make you feel uncomfortable, it can actually make intercourse painful by crowding everything up in there. It can also make you irritable and cause your face to break out or if you're like me, your shoulders, which is just as bad. If you don't have time to take your favorite laxative and be sure it will take effect when you're still alone (there's nothing like an attack of diarrhea when you're in a cozy hotel room sharing one bathroom to kill the romantic mood), there's another trick you can do. Take a Fleet enema (yes, the kind you had as a little girl) and sit in a basin of warm water (or a bidet if you're lucky enough to have one) until the desired results are produced. This ought to unblock you sufficiently for even a long weekend and what's more you get a dividend . . . you don't have to worry about gas pains, sounds, or smells!

Another little hint: get enough sleep. This is not always easy but even a tiny nap fifteen or twenty minutes long will relax and refresh you. In fact a lot of specialists will tell you that short naps are the best way to keep refreshed and rested. For someone who's a night person like me, it's been a boon. It also does marvels for your complexion, all over!

CHAPTER TEN

EXTRA-SEXORY PERCEPTION

There can be no doubt in any halfway sensual person's mind for the need to set a scene for sex. At its simplest, rudimentary level, loosening up with a few drinks or a tranquilizer, if necessary can help make a smoother connection. Then there are the more complicated routes to "get into the mood" with fantasy trip aids such as private porno flic watching or an erotic novel. Whatever way suits you to make the barriers fall and create a receptive atmosphere, there are certain physical contacts which are especially helpful to women. While some of these suggestions will seem obvious if you think about it a little, you will realize that just because of that, they are often overlooked. Nothing can put off a woman's possibility to enjoy sex more than getting "right into it" before she's had the proper amount of the kind of priming she needs. Here's my list.

FONDLING: SLOW TOUR OF THE PLEASURE ZONES—This is another way to describe what we all did as youngsters when we went out on "heavy" dates and referred to as *necking* and *petting*. There is nothing quite like this favorite old-fashioned pastime and certainly nothing to replace it. With the new sexuality and popular permissiveness, "Do you fuck?" or "Your place or mine?", there is not only no time for petting, but it is considered downright corny. Don't be done out of it; it serves us women well. Start fondling in the garage or make him stop somewhere on the way home. Arrange situations where jumping into the sack just isn't possible and induce your guy to get into some "light" petting or "heavy" necking whichever way you'd like to look at it. I like to sneak my hand into my lover's lap at the movies or nuzzle up to him real close while watching TV. Make the obvious places out of bounds—it makes things more interesting.

ORAL TENDERNESS—Not to be confused with oral lovemaking. This is caressing which is done with the lips and tongue instead of the hand. For instance, keep your tiniest bikini panties on and have your lover just run his lips and tongue down your back starting with the nape of the neck. Then have him proceed to the shoulder blades and on southward. I think you'll find this little exercise delicious and make you beg for more. Set up a few boundaries like no fair taking off the panties until you cry Uncle or Aunt if you prefer. This is a dynamite game and one area you mustn't allow him to miss is your armpit. This may take you farther than you think.

VIBRATORS FOR BOTH SOLOS AND DUETS—Vibrators can be fun, there's no question about that. But they can also be something else, a sexual aid for self-education and exploration. Using a vibrator at a very low speed and merely running the blunt button-shaped nozzle up and down the arm can reveal some very sensitive areas to you: the area just above the elb… instance, and the upper arm just below the sho… Another nice thing about vibrators is that they not … titillate the skin and its sensitivity but the muscles underneath also which have quite another, different kind of sensitivity. I'll let you in on one other big secret—once the guys get used to them, they turn on to them, too. One night, when your guy's in a particularly receptive mood, get him to lie on his stomach and gently run the vibrator nozzle over his buttocks. See if you don't get some interesting results with that one!

PORNOGRAPHY IN MOVIES AND PIX—Never underestimate the power of a so-called dirty picture. I was with an American group in a tour bus visiting the churches and cathedrals of Rome when I noticed the driver was showing something to the men in the group on the sly. I asked him to show me too, and he winked and said "Anything you say, signorina!" They were dirty pictures, of course. I asked him if he made a lot on the side selling those and he laughed out loud: "On the side! Cara signorina, it's the bus driving which is on the side. The only reason I took the job driving was to meet many people to sell my pictures. You see people who like to look at churches are the best customers for dirty pictures." I never understood the logic in his remark but the fact was he was making a fine living from the kind of people you would least expect to be interested in "that sort of thing." For a lot of people pornography is a turn-on and you can get pix or flicks almost anywhere. Any "sex" magazine will have addresses for you and the effect of a private showing of home movies can be very explosive. Also if you're trying to suggest something special to your beau that you don't want to come right out with, showing him some photos or films on the subject might just do the trick.

TALKING SEXY—This is not so easy as it seems since

the trick here is to do it out of context. The idea is to work on the imagination and stir the fires of anticipation to a blaze. One great way to do that is when you're in a situation with other people at a dinner party or otherwise in public. Whisper into your guy's ear something like: "Hey babe, I just thought you'd like to know that I shaved my pussy for you today," or "I'm not wearing panties." I like to send notes at dinner parties. I'll slip my guy a billet doux and walk away to another part of the room and check his reaction. A typical note is: "I'm imagining what a kick I'd get out of slipping my hand into your fly with all these people around." I usually get a rise with this one.

AURAL SEXUALITY—The impact of sounds on the sexual imagination should not be underrated. The big record companies know this and they spend millions developing voices and electronic effects that spell sex. It's very hard to know why we form sexual associations with certain tunes, or certain quality of voice or style of singing, but we do, all of us. Perhaps because of songs or sounds we heard when we felt our first sexual longings. Or perhaps even before that, before memory, when close and safe at mothers' breast, a tune she sang or her quality of voice registered deep in our unconscious memory. You quickly find out which sounds turn you on and with a little effort, you'll discover your lover's aural sex-spot. Create your own hit parade at home and get in the mood before getting into the sack.

SEXY SURROUNDINGS AND/OR PROPS—This may sound old-hat but making love on a fur throw was one of my favorite things. People used to walk into my living room and see this fur throw casually draped over the sofa or in front of the fire and say things like "Ah, I bet you have a lot of fun with that, ha,ha,ha." Well, you know I did. Lying bare-ass on that soft furry stuff was sensational. But then I developed an allergy to the adored prop and had to give it away. Too much of a good thing, I suppose. What kind of setting turns you on? Have you ever tried a sleazy hotel room with mirrors all over the place? Or how about satin sheets? They're too slippery for me but I have friends who swear by them. A friend of mine had a water bed in his den (king-sized, of course) which he kept nice and soft. The floating effect while making love was spectacular. Your positions are limited in this set-up but the sensation is fantastic.

S & M EXCHANGES—The S&M scene (Sadistic & Masochistic) has been the subject of much pornographic literature and flics/pix. We cannot help but have absorbed some of these images into our sexual subconscious. Just watching "normal" commercial movies on TV or in moviehouses will give us enough S&M material to feed our curiosities and imaginations. You may be curious about this aspect of lovemaking and if so, why not try it out following two rules: a) do it with someone who is willing and who you trust and b) exchange roles, one time you're S and the next, you're M. A friend once gave me a very fine leathered cat-o-nine-tails as a lark, he said it was to go with my leather boots. I got devilish one night and asked my lover to use it on my backside as we made love that way. Afterward I used it on him, lightly of course, no great red welts for days or anything like that. Being wicked was great fun. Another fun way to freak out is tying someone's hands behind their back and making them the prisoner of your fun and games.

FANTASIES COME TRUE—The S&M game is acting out a fantasy, of course, but I am thinking of less kinky fantasies right now. I had a lover who was a wonderful actor and he taught me to play his favorite fantasy: we would imagine that we were two other people, often characters out of a favorite movie. We would reenact bits of dialogue or love scenes from the movie, or we would imagine scenes the characters might have had. You can really get involved with this sort of thing if it catches on.

For instance, once we got dressed for the occasion: he wore a gabardine raincoat and dark hat and became Humphrey Bogart in *Casablanca*. I wore a white suit and did my best with a Swedish accent to become Ingrid Bergman. The scene ended with me saying, "You'll have to decide for both of us, Rick." Guess what he decided?

Another great fantasy trip is reading out loud from sexy parts of plays or novels. A great scene is the one between Blanche Dubois and Stanley Kowalski in *A Streetcar Named Desire* which ends with his sweeping her up in his arms to carry her off and make love to her while saying, "We've had this date with each other from the beginning."

EXHIBITIONISM—This is a tried and tested way to turn yourself and your guy on. We all know the effect of exposing a little bit of something suggestive, but there are all kinds of twists possible on this one.

A famous novelist describes a scene on a beach where he and his new love are invited to doff their suits and jump in naked with everyone else. She declines and he is relieved. However she waits until everyone else had come out and is sitting on the beach sunning before she calmly walks into the water and becomes the focus of attention. Once assured of having captured everyone's gaze, she stops far enough out for details to be suggested, not spelled out, and takes off her suit. Then she does a few well-chosen ballet positions with much raising of the leg and arching of the back. The writer tells about how he had never been so excited in his whole life. The description is quite exciting for the reader, too.

Sexy underwear is a form of exhibitionism that should

not be overlooked. I remember being at a girlfriend's apartment one day as she packed her husband's suitcase for a short vacation they were taking together. His underwear was neatly stacked and I noticed it was all white boxer shorts. I asked her if she had ever thought of getting her husband bikini underwear in different colors instead of that awful stuff. She replied "What for? Nobody sees it!" I thought, she really didn't know what a treat she was missing. Neither did he, for that matter.

There is a legendary story told about Billie Rose's famous nightclub, The Diamond Horseshoe. Apparently he ordered the most exquisite Irish linen lace for the bloomers of his long-stemmed Roses, as his dancers were called. One day as he watched a rehearsal of the Can-Can, he bragged about this to a friend. The friend was astonished and said, "What're you doing that for? Nobody in the audience knows they're wearing expensive Irish linen on their ass!" Rose replied, "But they know."

The moral of this story is when you know you look good, you *feel* good. This applies to knowing you look sexy, too. It makes you feel sexy. When I'm wearing a cut-out bra with the nipples exposed, it makes me feel sexy, even though I'm dressed and nobody else could possibly know it. When I just happen to mention it to my guy in public, however, it's a turn-on for both of us.

The fact that something we're wearing or saying or doing is turning somebody else on, will excite us also. So whether it's dressing in leather, or a scuba suit, whether it's playing "Doctor" or "Little Red Riding Hood," nothing is too silly if the participants are willing and eager to explore the far reaches of active, creative imagination.

CHAPTER ELEVEN

KICKS & KINKS

SCENE: Janie's husband liked to make love to two women at the same time. His first initiation to sex was with two women (prostitutes), and it was his favorite combination ever after. When Janie married Sam she knew nothing about this even though they had been lovers a whole year prior to their wedding. So when he finally worked up the courage to tell her he would like to invite other girls into their bedroom, it came as a bit of a surprise. Janie knew enough about psychology to realize that Sam must have felt guilty about it otherwise he would have brought it up much earlier. He denied this, saying he just didn't want to shock her and lose her love. She decided to go along.

At first it was a novelty and once she got over her inhibitions she didn't mind too much. After all she thought, this is the age of swap parties and orgies and swinging, so let's try it all. Soon it became clear that Sam really didn't want to make love any other way. There had to be another girl along for him to be interested in Janie at all. This got to be annoying at first and then frightening. The truth was that Sam didn't want her anymore, he just wanted her to be a foil for a new girl. She put her foot down one day and insisted he see a psychotherapist. It took a lot of visits to the shrink and a lot of patience from Janie, but Sam worked out his problems. As soon as he realized that what he thought was just a kick had become a sexual crutch, he could deal with it.

As far as the limits of lovemaking are concerned, within large boundaries, anything goes. Those boundaries involve the rule of thumb of not inflicting pain on an unwilling partner and seeing to it that the activities end up ideally in satisfaction for both. The whole concept of perversions has been pretty much exploded as being arbitrary rules established by up-tight people. Anything goes between two consenting people if it turns them on. The famous German psychiatrist Krafft-Ebbing, who died in 1902, was the author of the term "paranoia." He set the freedom of sexual expression back a hundred years by pasting the label "perversion" on everything that didn't turn him on. Words like *sadism* and *masochism* are labels and as far as I'm concerned so is the word "normal" in the mouths of certain people. The way to determine normal is not by contrast to what you have decided is abnormal, but by asking "what does this behavior do to this person?" Naturally there are people who are crippled by their fantasies. But couples who can only do it mama-papa style, as fast as they can, under the covers, in the dark, are crippled too. Fantasies are limitless and acting them out can be a mutually liberating game, permission for one, trust from the other.

We women almost always assume that when there is a problem, it is our fault. It is part of our conditioning to feel that the happiness of the couple is our responsibility and when things go wrong we have to change in order to put them right. There are less dramatic ways in which this situation arises in sexual matters and maybe you'll find some familiar.

A man I knew was really turned on to women-together scenes. He subscribed to lesbian reviews and had huge collections of pix and flix of women making love. He was always trying to get his wife's friends into bed with them. His wife went along with his games as long as she could but one day when he started bringing in girls off the street, she had to tell him that his obsession was driving her mad. He laughed at the use of the word obsession and called her jealous. She then asked his good friends to tell him straight out how tired they all were with his constant allusions to women together. They did, because when she told them that her husband had become impotent with her and she was leaving him, they knew he needed help. He never got any and they split up.

Naturally there are situations that raise questions.

A situation that many women speak of and wonder about is one in which the man wants anal intercourse and the woman does not. I have rarely met a woman who has honestly said she liked anal intercourse a whole lot. Most men, on the other hand, do enjoy this form of lovemaking and there are a number of reasons for this. The anus is tighter and therefore grips the penis better or at least more firmly than the vagina does. Another reason (and this can get us into kinks) is the very fact that the woman is reticent and that penetration there is uncomfortable, distasteful perhaps, even painful, and makes it that much more of a conquest.

Now I want to go on record as saying there is nothing wrong (if right or wrong are terms anyone should use) with anal intercourse between consenting partners. If a man wants it, that doesn't make him queer or kinky. If a woman wants it too, that doesn't make her a freak. If she doesn't want it and he insists, the waters are getting muddy.

Great care has to be taken with anal intercourse. A lubricant should always be used such as K-Y jelly or lots of saliva or the like. Your guy should ease his penis inside *very slowly* and this is important because delicate tissues could be torn and cause a lot of pain. A good way to prepare for this spicy pastime is for your guy to use his fingers for a while until your muscles down there begin to stretch easily. Every now and then during the day, you can prime yourself with your own fingers just to help things along. There are devices that you can actually wear or sleep with that are designed to stretch the anal muscles and prepare them for intercourse. Your doctor won't know about them probably, but again any sex magazine will have a mail order advertisement for "sexual aids."

A big no-no to anal intercourse is doing it simultaneously with vaginal intercourse. Every porno I've ever read has a required sequence where she's squealing with joy as he moves "with swift strokes from one opening to the other." Hogwash! for most cases anyway. Of course if you are very excited and very lubricated, you might get away with this and get pleasure out of it but chances are you won't want it as a steady practice. You also take the chance of getting an infection in the vagina as a result. The vagina has special microbes in it which fight infections. The rectum does not, and is in fact full of germs harmful to the vagina. The result can be trichomonodes or the like. One or the other, not both at the same time.

Again if you get a kick out of this every once in a while, why not? However if your guy insists on it, likes it better than any other way, gets pleasure out of forcing his way in, hurting you, and so on, chances are he's got a problem.

Has he ever asked you to dress a certain way for love? Black garter belt and see-through underwear and the like? This can be a turn-on for everybody and once in a while it's great fun. Remember if you know you're doing something that really turns someone on, it's exciting for you too and that's great. However if it gets to the point where he just can't get it up unless you're in a crash helmet and thigh-high boots, he just may have a problem.

The situation can be reversed in that it might be you who wants "something special." You may have seen something or read something you want to try out. You may have a foot fetish like me and want your feet oiled and caressed for a while. Why not? If your guy objects on the grounds that "he doesn't do that sort of thing" or worse yet, he calls you sick because you want to try something different, don't for heaven's sake be intimidated. If he's uptight, that's his problem. Help him to overcome it of course, but don't make it yours.

I want to stress an important point about fantasies and fetishes. They are a perfectly normal part of lovemaking and it's great to be able to throw oneself into acting them out naturally. I contend there is nothing unnatural in any aspect of sex unless it causes pain, moral or bodily, to an unwilling partner. If ground rules are set up and everyone is agreed, all systems should be go. You may ask what happens if your partner refuses. It depends on the grounds of his refusal. Even if something doesn't inspire him or turns him somewhat off, he should be willing to make an honest try at it for your sake. If he makes a try and is still turned off, you have to determine if his reaction is inhibition (which can be corrected) or aversion (which is a lot harder to change). If he reacts on moral grounds, in other words he thinks what you want to try is "dirty" or "bad," you've got a lot of re-education to do on him before you can get past Go.

What is the difference between a kick and a kink? Let me illustrate it with a case I knew about. Sara had a new lover she was very happy with. His imagination in lovemaking, far from making her wary about kinks, tended more to spark her imagination as well. One day he fished a pair of her unwashed panties from the clothes hamper and took them to bed. As he made love to her he kept the panties close at hand and kept smelling them and making her smell them, kept assuring her that she should be turned on by her own pussy smell as much as he was. As the days went by he kept asking for more panties and kept making her promise not to wash out a pair for a week so the aromas could be really pungent. Finally he couldn't get an erection without the panties and when she caught him masturbating (when he thought he was alone) into a pair of panties, she knew she was face to face with a kink, not a kick.

Essentially a kick should make things spicier and heighten the goings on. It should be an added attraction, not the whole show. When the show can't go on without it, as happened in Sara's case, the name of the game is kink or hang-up. When this happens it's therapist time because the origins of sexual dependencies can usually only be ironed out with the help of some form of therapy. Don't make them your problems, since their roots go back long before you entered the scene.

CHAPTER TWELVE

SEX WITHOUT ORGASM????

SCENE: Miriam was in her forties, happily married to her second husband, a successful career woman with two teen-age children. She and John made love regularly and during the twelve years of their marriage never tired of each other in or out of bed. "We made love once or twice a week and during relaxed circumstances with more time for each other, as on vacation for example, we made love more often. I never had an orgasm and until I started reading about it everywhere, I never missed it." John knew this for she never had faked climax, she merely said it didn't matter.

They started reading the books widely publicized on female sexuality and orgasm. John thought Miriam ought to go visit a sexologist and see whether treatment could help her to greater pleasure in sex through orgasm. She agreed, "Why not, it's worth a try. I've got nothing to lose." She went to the clinic for elaborate testing, had sessions with therapists, did a lot of reading and all the other things she had to do.

After a few months she announced to her therapist she was dropping the whole thing. When asked why by her very surprised doctor, she said: "It's all become mechanical, the spontaneity is gone. John's trying so hard to *do* all the right things. I'm trying too hard to feel something *else*, something new, I've stopped feeling what I used to love to feel . . . close, warm, loved. We're making love to our sexual organs, not each other."

I think Miriam was trying to say that she felt a difference between *making love* and *feeling loved.* We shouldn't make love to sexual organs but to people. Maybe Miriam dropped out too soon. Or maybe she felt that what she had was enough and the delicate balance of tenderness, intimacy, sexual closeness, was going to be upset by mechanically trying for more. Many women would urge Miriam to carry on and keep trying but no one can persuade her that she is getting nothing out of lovemaking without orgasm, because she knows differently. There is nothing abnormal about her, she has discovered what's right for her, that's all.

Another interesting case is the one of Anne who had just had a hysterectomy at the age of thirty-eight. She was feeling very low because now there was no question of her being able to have the baby she had thought of having during the five years of marriage to David. Partly she was afraid David might think her less "feminine" as a result. Also the doctor had told her it would take about six weeks for the stitches at the end of her vagina to heal so lovemaking would be out of the question for the duration.

David was very understanding and helpful around the house after her return from the hospital but still her depression would not disappear. One day finally, during a crying jag, she admitted her fears and to her surprise he laughed. He called her a silly dunce and confessed that he never really desired the baby she kept thinking of having and he always thought that menstrual periods were a bore anyway. As for her femininity he couldn't speak for her subjective feelings but "I've never found you more desirable and I'm delighted that I'll never have to worry about birth control anymore."

That night they made love, not in the traditional sense meaning the old in-and-out but in the sense of communicating the emotions each brought out in the other. Anne spent hours caressing and being caressed. Pleasure rolled over her body like gentle breezes, not tidal waves. She and David murmured and kissed alternately and endlessly. Not in their wildest night of repeated intercourse had they ever been closer.

Anne and David discovered sexual tenderness by accident. A lot of people never discover it at all because they are so preoccupied with reaching orgasmic bliss as fast as possible. Part of the rush to orgasm is due to performance anxiety which the new sexuality has brought on. With all the books and articles telling us if we don't have numerous paroxysms of orgasmic pleasure with each partner each time we make love, we are either incompetent, ignorant, abnormal, or all three. With this kind of pressure it is easy to see why the forest was lost for the trees.

By forest, I'm referring to pleasure in the form of tenderness and intimacy. There are times when a touch on the hand will express more love and adoration than even oral sex can and I'm sure you've experienced just such a touch. I believe that lovemaking is first and foremost communication, the need to say in physical terms, I love you or I need you. There are those who will doggedly insist that the purpose of lovemaking is to beget children; I would reply that procreation is a side effect of lovemaking, not its main purpose. If it were the main purpose, indeed the only purpose, we women would react like female animals to sex; they're not interested unless they can conceive. The males just have to wait around for a bitch in heat before they can get any action.

Others would say that the purpose of lovemaking is to relieve sexual pressure and that would make orgasm absolutely essential. But for centuries most women didn't have orgasms, didn't know they could have them, thought and were taught they shouldn't have pleasure at all. And yet, they went on making love. Sexual relief is a male problem, not a female one. The testicles make sperm cells constantly in human and animal males and as the sacs fill with sperm they begin to ache, putting pressure on the male to empty them. He has two ways to do this if he is human or ape, and that is masturbation or fornication. The difference then between lovemaking and fornication is that the former is a form of communication, a language. And the latter is merely a biological function. But let's look at the apes for a moment.

The apes are the closest link to humans on the evolutionary scale and observation of them has been very edifying. Apes like all other animals mate with the male mounting the female from the back, commonly known as dog-style. Humans are the only animals who mate face to face. However apes pair off into couples and form family units. The males become not only attached to the little ones but attentive and tender with them. They mate not only when the female is in heat but often outside of her heat-menstrual period (in animals conception takes place during the menstrual period). They cuddle with each other, and while they do not kiss on the lips (neither did we humans until someone made it stylish) they do kiss and nibble each other on the ear, neck, and so forth. If they lose a baby either by natural death or to a predatory animal, they express sorrow and console each other. If one is sick, the other will care and fuss and, yes, look worried. In other words, even in apes, tenderness, an expression of love not involving intercourse, exists.

To get back to humans, particularly female humans, I think the very fact that women have always made love (love for love's sake, not just conjugal duty) long before they knew about orgasms, is proof that it is possible to enjoy sex without them. Of course there must have been lucky ones among the countless women in history who happened on orgasm by chance. But all the others who were enjoying it without orgasm were nevertheless enjoying it. That doesn't mean that in the long run they didn't pay the price for years and years of reaching sexual peaks without release from tension. I'm sure they did and each age found a new name for the nervousness this tension brought about. But still they made love. Why?

You may have heard the expression that with men sexual attraction starts in the groin and with women it starts in the head. I think there is some truth to this saying in that for most women the idea of sex comes after other areas of attraction are already in motion. A man's wit, sense of humor, intelligence, charm have usually struck some sensitive areas before a woman starts imagining him as a sexual partner. With men the physical attributes of a woman usually make the first points. That's what men mean when they try to explain an infidelity to their wives by saying "it didn't mean anything." In other words the other woman was just a body.

Why women tend to get more "involved" with an affair than men do is probably because more of their curiosity, instincts, desires to share get involved. I think the desire to give and to share is very strong in women in that it is this desire which makes lovemaking a necessary part of their lives, even without orgasm.

Mind you I think the desires to give and share are part of the male personality make-up as well. Early in childhood however society starts to shape and manipulate, the role-playing is taught and even before school begins (where the screws really tighten) the masculine and feminine stamps begin to draw their lines. Aggressiveness and assertiveness in girls is discouraged; selflessness, helpfulness, subservience are applauded traits. In boys everything having anything to do with tenderness and sensitivity is frowned upon. Boys must learn to play hard, win fairly if possible, but win, and develop physical and mental strength with which to dominate. Is it any wonder that they are brutes at lovemaking until a woman with patience and know-how enough can teach them the A-B-Cs. With a little help most men can relearn sensitive and responsive tenderness in love because it is part of the male instincts also, the apes prove this.

If all it took to be satisfied and happy sexually was an orgasm each time love is made, all men would be divinely happy, wouldn't they? With enough manipulation of the penis every normally constructed man can come to orgasm. Why do men fall in love then? Why do they have passionate attachments to one woman and commit themselves to marriage and a certain degree of exclusivity to that woman? The answer would appear to be quite simple: there is much, much more to joy in lovemaking than orgasm, even for men.

In sex institutes all over the country hundreds of thousands of people have been tested and their reactions recorded concerning sexual responsiveness. Women who have not gone into the testing clinics but have given candid answers to questions on confidential questionnaires echo the findings of the clinics: female orgasm can become a behavioral pattern—if a woman begins to have them at a reasonably young age she will continue to need them. If she has had good sex, loving, security-making sex without orgasm for enough years, she will not feel the need for them nor consciously suffer the lack of them.

Reports from older couples will bear out the validity of the notion that sex can still be pleasurable and desired even without orgasm for either a man or woman. Older people are coming out of the closet as far as talking about their sex lives. Masters and Johnson have proved with their testing and interviewing that older people are not only capable of, but continue to desire, sex play well into their seventies and eighties. Apparently if you keep the body active in that area, the body functions very well. If as a person gets older, they drop out of sex entirely, for any length of time, getting back into it can cause difficulties. But if sex has been regular, all systems can function.

Now what is interesting in this is that the pressure on men to ejaculate diminishes with the years as their production of sperm drops. So older men's *biological* need to make love disappears. The need that motivates older people to lovemaking is the psychological, emotional one. At the end of life men and women come together again, as the role playing of "Me Tarzan, you Jane" no longer makes any sense. They come together and hold each other, caress each other, as a way of saying "I love you. After all the years and all the difficulties shared, love is still here."

With the new sexuality and the knowledge of the importance of sex, we women must assert our right to orgasm. We must set ourselves the duty to train our bodies and our lovers to help us to orgasm. There is no question in my mind that this is one of the legitimate demands of lovemaking.

Still, if I had to choose right now between orgasm without love, and love without orgasm, I would not hesitate. I would choose love: tenderness, intimacy, devotion, respect, all the things that make the difference between being an animal and being a human.

EPILOGUE:

STILL A LONG WAY TO GO

The Pill, the Sexual Revolution, the New Sexuality are all giant steps forward toward equal rights for women in the sack. However the sack is just one part of our lives and very often it is the stage on which many other aspects of our lives are acted out. A very savvy friend of mine who explains why she always brings a lover to bed on the first date says, "That's where the truth about a guy's personality is revealed. In bed everyone shows their true colors. It's the best way and certainly the fastest way, of knowing whether I even want to see him a second time."

The underlying attitudes of society concerning women certainly affect not only men's attitudes toward us, but our attitudes toward ourselves. If we accept even unconsciously to be treated as second-class citizens in our schools, jobs, and governments, it will be that much harder for us to demand equal rights sexually. As long as marriage vows and divorce laws treat women as men's possessions, the waters will be muddied for us sexually.

We are living in a very exciting period of transition right now where perhaps the last stages of the struggle for women's equality are being worked out. The traumatic effects of this particular moment in history should not be underrated. It is a difficult time for us as we try to strike a livable balance between our determination to be considered as equals and our desires for happiness with men who have not yet grasped the urgency of our needs. Men and women are moving at different speeds in the long march toward the goal of loving equals and sometimes our calls for cooperation and concessions take on the strident tones of criticism and recrimination. It is not easy to do battle all day and then expect adversaries to embrace in bed at night in an atmosphere of trust and love.

But somewhere we must draw a line. In some area we must be able to call a permanent halt to further insult and humiliation. I believe the area should be the sexual one since it is here that our rights have been usurped the longest. We are not sex machines to be turned on and off at will, we are not merely walking, talking genitalia coyly called "the weaker sex." We are human beings capable of receiving as well as giving, and that means love and pleasure as well as sex.

So this book then is a call for pleasure in a clear, female voice, sounding not only the love and patience that have come to be expected of us, but also the determination and independence we have come to discover in ourselves.

REFERENCES

Barbach, Lonnie Garfield. *For Yourself, The Fulfillment of Female Sexuality*. Doubleday. 1976.

The Boston Women's Health Book Collective. *Our Bodies, Ourselves*. Simon & Schuster, 1971, 1973.

Calderone, Mary S. *Release from Sexual Tensions*. Random House, 1960.

Comfort, Alex. *The Joy of Sex*. Crown Publishers, Inc., 1972.

Deutsch, Ronald M. *The Key to Feminine Response in Marriage*. Random House, 1968.

Dreifus, Claudia. *Woman's Fate: Raps From a Feminist Consciousness-Raising Group*. Bantam Books, 1973.

Dworkin, Andrea. *Woman Hating*. E. P. Dutton & Co. Inc., 1974.

Ellis, Albert. *The American Sexual Tragedy*. Lyle Stuart, 1962.

Fisher, Seymour. *The Female Orgasm*. Basic Books, 1973.

Frankfort, Ellen. *Vaginal Politics*. Bantam Books, 1972.

Freud, S. *The Basic Writings of Sigmund Freud*. Random House, 1938.

Friedan, Betty. *The Feminine Mystique*. Dell Publishing Co., 1964.

Greer, Germaine. *The Female Eunuch*. Bantam Books, 1970.

Hite, Shere. ed., *Sexual Honesty, By Women for Woman*. Warner Paperback Library, 1974.

Horney, Karen. *Feminine Psychology*. W. W. Norton & Co., Inc., 1967.

Kaplan, Helen Singer. *The New Sex Therapy*. Quadrangle, The New York Times Book Co., 1974.
Kegel, A. H. "Sexual Functions of the Pubococcygeus Muscle." *Western Journal of Surgery, Obstetrics and Gynecology*. 1952.
———. "Active Exercise of the Pubococcygeus Muscle." *Progress in Gynecology*. Grune and Stratton, 1950.
Kinsey, Alfred. *Sexual Behavior in the Human Male*. W. B. Saunders, 1948.
———. *Sexual Behavior in the Human Female*. W. B. Saunders, 1953.
Koedt, Anne. *The Myth of the Vaginal Orgasm*. New England Free Press, 1970.
Krafft-Ebbing. *Psychopathia Sexualis*. London, 1893.
Masters and Johnson. *Human Sexual Inadequacy*. Little, Brown and Company, 1971.
———. *Human Sexual Response*. Little, Brown and Company, 1966.
Mead, Margaret. *Male and Female: A Study of the Sexes in a Changing World*. William Morrow, 1949.
Millet, Kate. *Sexual Politics*. Avon, 1971.
Oliven, J. F. *Sexual Hygiene and Pathology*. Lippincott, 1955.
Popenoe, P. *Marital Counselling With Special Reference to Frigidity*. American Institute of Family Relations, Publication No. 502, Los Angeles.
Reich, Wilhelm. *The Function of the Orgasm*. Farrar, Straus and Giroux, 1946.
Seaman, Barbara. "Liberated Orgasm." *Ms.* 1972.
Sherfey, Mary Jane. *The Nature and Evolution of Female Sexuality*. Vintage Books, Random House, 1966, 1972.
Vatsayana. *Kamasutra*. Lancer Books, 1964.